Bee Keeping

A Novices Guide

Words and pictures
by David Wootton

PUBLISHING

First published in Great Britain in 2010 by:
David Wootton Publishing.

Copyright 2010 David Wootton.
Copyright all photography: David Wootton Photography.
Additional Photography: Helen Wootton.

Photo Credit - Honey Bee with varroa mite
Stephen Ausmus: United States Department of Agriculture.

David Wootton has asserted his moral rights to be identified as the author.

A CIP Catalogue of this book is available from the British Library.

ISBN: 978-0-9566877-0-8

Designed and typeset by
www.chandlerbookdesign.co.uk

Printed in Great Britain by
Ashford Colour Press Ltd.

Acknowledgements

A big thank you to Terry and Lorraine Gibson, my mentors. First for the numerous phone calls and emails I made to them, as I learnt the art of beekeeping and secondly for very kindly helping me with this book. Without their expertise and patience, it would not have been possible.

Thank you also to my wife, Helen, for her patience as I wrote this book and spent many evenings in the shed building hives and frames. I also apologize for the times I have asked her to assist me with a quick job, saying no need to kit up and then she ends up being stung. This has happened on more than one occasion.

Thank you also to Mike Jervis and Mike Waldron fellow regulars at the Hare Arms who kindly read the book translating my words and grammar from Norfolk into English.

Contents

Introduction

For a few years I had watched a wild colony of honey bees coming and going from a hollow brick gate pillar near my home. I had even seen them swarm, without knowing their reason for this. I was fascinated by the bees' activities and this led me to think it would be fun to have my own hives. Having made this decision, I started researching how I would go about doing this. Numerous books, magazines and the internet gave me all manner of advice on how to get started. However the more I read the more daunting it all seemed, especially as some advice totally contradicted that of others. Having done much research I then took the necessary steps to become a beekeeper. Two years later I have 6 hives, my bees are thriving and giving me a bumper harvest of honey.

My research informed me that keeping a few colonies of bees was easy and relatively cheap. I do not wish to put anyone off keeping bees; but, you have to be committed as there is a lot more to it than some of the books and articles I read, lead you to believe. Please don't get me wrong as it is great fun and I have thoroughly enjoyed looking after my bees, but all the information you receive, can become a bit confusing. The terminology used can also be confusing, so for this reason I have written a comprehensive glossary, which I wish I had had at the time.

As a professional photographer I have been taking photographs regularly of my bees and bee keeping and was therefore fortunate to be able illustrate this book with my images. I felt that visually seeing the hive, equipment and steps you need to take would help in understanding what is required as a new beekeeper when fulfilling your dream of keeping honey bees on a small scale.

One thing you will learn is that every beekeeper has a different opinion on every aspect of beekeeping. I have heard that if you ask a question to 10 beekeepers you will get 10 different answers and this is probably correct. However, experimenting and finding what works for you is part of the pleasure of being the guardian of your own bees.

Most beekeeping books are written by experts who assume you know something about beekeeping. I was lucky to meet a couple, who with years of beekeeping experience, have kindly acted as my mentors as I learnt how to keep bees. They have also aided me in the writing of this book. This book is not an expert's view on how to keep bees, there are plenty of those. This is an aid to discovering the pleasure of how to keep bees written in layman's language and by someone who only a short while ago was in the same position you are in now. The book covers the advice I got, how I got it and the practical side to keeping bees which I have only just learnt. Thankfully I believe I have not made any major mistakes. My bees seem content with their coming and going from the hives and if success is measured on the quality of honey they have produced then I think I have succeeded.

Honey bee collecting nectar from a crocus flower.

Getting started

"don't be afraid to ask"

So you've made the biggest decision you are going to make in beekeeping and that's deciding to become a beekeeper. But what do you do now?

Don't worry I was in exactly the same position. I had sat for hours at my computer surfing the internet and you will no doubt do the same. But what really got me going was joining my local beekeeping association. I found my local association - the West Norfolk and King's Lynn Beekeeping Association (WNKLBA) with a quick search in Google. If you can't find yours by an internet search, go to your national beekeeping association website, most countries have one and they should be able to link you into your local association or club. There is no better place to start and as I found, your local association will run courses for beginners and during the winter months the theory courses are the perfect way to find out about your new hobby. These courses are designed to give you the basic knowledge about bees, the hive, inspections and how to get started.

Come the spring when the hives can be opened, the course continues allowing you to get your first practical experience of handling bees in a hive. It's a great experience lifting your first frame of active bees from a hive. There are so many advantages to joining your local association and I have found no negative ones.

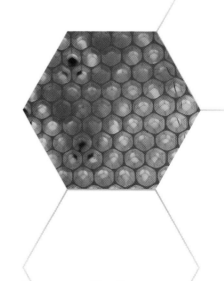

Beekeeper inspecting
frames in a super.

Joining your local association is not expensive and usually comes with third party liability and hive insurance. But the main advantage is that you get the opportunity to meet experienced beekeepers and all the ones I have met have been only too pleased to answer my questions. My course tutor said "The only stupid question is the one not asked ". This is true, so don't be afraid however stupid you think your question might be. The theory course I took was over three evenings, in which we were introduced to the honey bee via a Powerpoint presentation. Bees throughout their lives have a specific role within the hive. This is one aspect which is very important in beekeeping and for this reason I detail this in a subsequent chapter.

When spring arrived the association apiary, where the practical courses took place saw new members split into small groups each with an experienced beekeeper. First we were taught how to dress correctly, this helps if you want to avoid unnecessary stings and how to light our smokers without it going out just when you needed it. Once ready the roof of the hive was removed and we took our first look at the working innards. We each took turns to remove a couple of frames and having pointed out to us the working bees, the drones and if you're lucky, the queen. Inspecting the frames within the hive you will soon be able to spot the eggs, larvae, capped brood and pollen cells plus sealed honey cells.

If you are lucky you will meet an experienced beekeeper who will be willing to act as your mentor. I was fortunate enough to meet a married couple who have made starting up so much easier. It's great if you have someone on the end of the telephone or e-mail to answer questions if you are uncertain about some aspect.

Your association will also run other courses and events throughout the year. These courses go into more detail on specialist subjects, such as bee diseases, how to winter your bees, extracting honey and wax products etc. The more you can learn will only make keeping bees that much easier for you. Having completed your course you should now have the confidence to make a start. There is no rush as it will be some time before you can start your first colony of bees. However now is the time to start putting together the equipment you require in preparation. Some may wish to purchase their first hive ready assembled, complete with frames and foundation. I myself enjoy making my hives from pre-cut kits. I find it therapeutic spending the winter evenings in my shed building the hives rather than watching yet more celebrity reality shows on television. Anyone with an ounce of DIY skills can do it.

Hints & tips

- Find yourself a mentor

- Build your own hives and frames, it's enjoyable and cheaper

New beekeepers and instructor at a local association apiary opening a National hive.

The hive

"where it all happens"

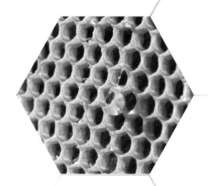

There are a number of different types of hive that you can buy. Names you may come across are the Langstroff, Smith, Dadant and Commercial hives. Each country seems to have their own designs and preferences. Beekeepers are also experimenting with Top Bar hives which are traditionally used in Africa. However in the United Kingdom, the two most used hives are the National and WBC hives. The WBC is perhaps what we imagine a hive to look like, with its gable roof and slanting sides. This hive is double skinned, with the working part of the hive encased within an outer wooden wall. Some beekeepers like this, one for looks and because of the double skin, the timber used does not have to be so thick and heavy.

The majority of beekeepers in Britain though use the National Bee Hive. I decided on this version, basically because all the parts are easily purchased and can be switched between one hive and another. In general hive parts are not interchangeable, due to the different dimensions. The one exception to this being that frames can be swapped between WBC and National hives as their dimensions are identical. However, whichever type of hive you decide to use, the principles of their use are all basically the same, just the dimensions of the hive being different.

A bee hive is a layer of boxes. As bees tend to work upwards within the colony, the first or lowest box (brood box) is where the queen lays her eggs and the colony feeds and raises the bee larvae until they hatch. Above this, different layers of boxes are added in which the bees store their food (honey). By controlling where they store this honey enables us, the beekeeper to harvest it.

Having made your decision on the type of hive you want, you need to choose whether to build your hive. You can purchase a completed hive already constructed with frames included. Or you can buy pre-cut kits that with some time, glue and nails you can assemble yourself. I thoroughly enjoy building my own hives and frames and if you have any DIY skills you will not find it too difficult. When purchasing your first hive it is advisable to buy the best you can afford. The best is widely acknowledged as being made of Red Cedar wood. Pine and other types of wood are perfectly acceptable, but in general, need much more care and maintenance. New on the market are plastic hives. However I have heard that these can have a lack of ventilation and therefore create condensation problems within the hive. This might be due to plastic being non-porous and therefore does not breath like wood. The big advantage though is that they will last for many years without any maintenance.

1. Flat roof
2. Crown board under roof
3. 2nd super
4. 1st super
5. Queen excluder
6. Half size brood box
7. Brood box
8. Entrance block
9. Wire mesh floor
10. Hive stand with alighting board
11. Legs

The National hive

"part by part"

When I started it was confusing trying to understand which part of a hive did what, plus some beekeepers give each part alternative names. I have therefore written brief details with photographs to help you recognise the individual parts and their practical uses.

1. Hive stand and landing board

This is the bottom part of the hive. Often fitted with a landing board (alighting board) for the bees. Shorts legs can be fitted, but I have found building my own stands raises the hive, so I don't get back ache from bending down to it.

2. Wire mesh floor and varroa mite board

The wire mesh floor is next placed on to the hive stand. Your bees as they move about within the hive will drop pieces of dirt, wax and comb, plus varroe mites as they die or are groomed off will fall through the mesh. This debris will collect on to the mite board which slides in below. Regular inspection of this will enable you to see the level of any infestation. The mesh floor also enables ventilation as a flow of air through the hive is essential.

3. Entrance block

The entrance block is a piece of wood which fits into the front of the hive. Its narrow opening allows bees to come and go. When the colony is small the narrow entrance is easily protected against any intruders. As the colony grows the entrance block can be partially pulled out to give a larger entrance and at times can be fully removed, though some experts advocate that as wild bees have a narrow entrance to protect, a hive should also have one and that the entrance block should be left in place all year round.

4. Empty brood box

The brood box, also known as the deep box, is where the majority of the colony will live on frames. This is where the queen will lay her eggs and the young bees will feed the larvae. The box is a dark sanctuary for the bees and kept at a constant 35°C (95f) in temperature. In the winter this is where your colony will cluster to see out the winter months.

1 **Hive stand.** With Landing board. Fitted to homemade raised stand.

2 **Wire mesh floor/varroa mite board.** Board can be slid out for inspections.

3 **Entrance block.** Showing narrow entrance when in place.

4 **Empty brood box.** With metal runners which frames sit on.

National hives with gable and flat roofs.

5. Brood box frames and dummy board

Within the brood box, the beekeeper places wooden frames with wax foundation. A brood box generally has 11 to 12 frames in place. I personally have 11 frames plus a dummy board. It is on these frames that your bees will draw out the wax foundation to create the cells in which the queen will lay her eggs and the workers will store nectar and pollen. In very strong colonies the brood box can be increased in size by adding a super and frames on top. Adding a super as a ½ sized brood box, will give extra space for the queen to lay her eggs. The dummy board is used as the first end frame, first to be removed when doing an inspection and therefore the last to be returned to the hive. As a piece of wood, the bees don't tend to be on it, so when closing the hive, you can add this without rolling and damaging your bees.

6. Queen excluder

Once your bee colony has expanded they will need more room to leave their stores of honey. As a beekeeper we want the stores of honey to be clear of any eggs and larvae. So before adding a super, a queen excluder is added between the brood box and the super. Queen excluders are made of plastic, galvanized steel or wire mesh. What they all have in common is that the worker bees can pass through, but not the larger queen and drones. She will therefore always remain in the brood box laying her eggs.

7. Empty super with metal castellations

When your colony needs the extra space to expand into, this is when the beekeeper adds a super. A super is the same dimension as the brood box, but not as deep. Shallow frames are placed in it and these can be spaced using plastic or metal spacers. My preference is to use metal castellations, which are attached to the side of the super, with slots to take the individual frames and spacing them at the correct distance.

8. Super with 10 frames

My choice is to use 10 frames in a super. Supers can contain between 8-10 frames, personal preference of the beekeeper being the deciding factor. Depending on the season, you will need to keep an eye on how quickly your bees are filling the super. During a good supply of pollen and nectar it is not unknown for bees to fill a super within a week. As your supers fill keep adding new ones, it is far better to have too many on than not enough.

5 **Brood box with frames.** Dummy board showing as the end frame.

6 **Queen excluder.** With slots running at right angles to the frames.

7 **Empty super with metal castellations.** Plastic or metal spacers can be attached to frames instead.

8 **Super with 10 frames.** Choice of 8 to 10 frames in your hive.

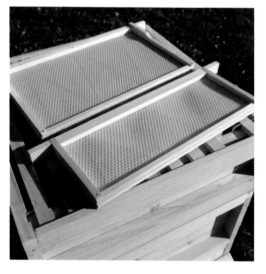

9 **Deep and shallow frames.** Wire supports can be seen in wax foundation.

10 **Crown board.** Showing holes for feeding or bee escapes.

11 **Flat roof.** Gable roofs are also available.

12 **Eke.** An empty super can also be used as a spacer.

9. Deep and shallow frames

The frames are where your bees will build their comb. Deep frames are used within the brood box and shallow frames in supers. When new, frames have wax foundation in them which the bees will draw out. Each sheet of wax foundation is wired to help rigidity and to hold them together when placed in a honey extractor. If you like comb honey it is possible to get unwired shallow foundation, this enables you to cut out blocks of honey to enjoy.

10. Crown board

In simple terms this is the ceiling of the hive and is the last thing to put on top of the boxes before putting the roof on. One or two holes are cut into the board; these are either feeding holes or used to place a bee escape when clearing bees out of the supers to extract the honey. Other than when feeding or clearing, the crown board holes remain covered. A piece of heavy card will do, however I had a local glazier hone the edges of some thick glass which I use to cover the holes.

11. Roof

As stated this is the top of the hive. Most National hives have a flat roof though if you wish to make you hive more attractive, gable roofs are available. Each roof is designed to keep water out and has ventilation ducts to enable the free flow of air through the hive.

12. Eke

An Eke is a shallow frame of wood, the same dimensions as the brood box and supers. It can be placed on top of the boxes to create a space between the tops of the frames and crown board for administering certain kinds of Varroa treatment or winter feed in the form of fondant. When administering treatment or fondant you will find the crown board and roof will not fit without one in place. An empty super can be used to serve the same function.

Making up a frame of foundation.

25

Equipment

"buy it as you need it"

There are a number the items of equipment which you will need from the start. This equipment will enable you make the necessary hive inspections in your first year.

1. Bee suit

There are numerous different suits on the market. I would suggest trying some on to see which you like best before buying. Some have a fitted round hat and veil whilst others have a Fencing style veil. You also have a choice of a full suit or smock. Make certain the elasticated cuffs fit snugly and also the suit has some useful pockets. I purchased a smock originally, but now have a full suit, having learnt that when you bend down the smock rides up and a bee can be trapped when you pull it down again. I learnt the hard way trapping two bees and being stung twice.

2. Smoker

One of your most important tools. Again there is a great choice of smokers to look at. All do the same thing, enabling you to blow cool smoke when you are inspecting your hives. The cheaper ones are galvanized steel and the most expensive are made of copper. They also come in different sizes, depending on the number of hives you have to inspect. As a beginner, you will not have a large apiary to inspect so purchase an average size one and the best you can afford.

3. Hive tool

This two ended tool is something you cannot work without when inspecting a hive. The tool is double ended. The sharper end is used for cracking the propolis seal the bees have made, when lifting off either the crown board and supers or scraping away any build up of wax and propolis from areas you do not want it. The hook end aids you in lifting out the frames from the hive. Generally you will find that you have the hive tool in your hand at all times.

4. Fuel for your smoker

You need a dry material which will smoulder rather than catch fire. It is possible to buy rolled cardboard smoke cartridges, however I find these burn too quickly and have burnt out before I am finished. I find old hessian sacking the best, as it smoulder's slowly allowing you to complete your hive inspection in plenty of time. Shredded cardboard packaging is also good, usually I put a little of this in with a scrunched up piece of hessian.

1 **Bee suit.** There are a variety of full length suits or smocks.

2 **Smoker.** Various sizes in stainless steel or copper.

3 **Hive tool**. You will need this to hand at all times.

4 **Fuel for smoker.** Hessian and or cardboard packaging.

5 **Gloves.** Leather and canvas gauntlets.

6 **Bee brush.** A soft haired brush to remove bees.

7 **Rapid feeder.** In place on hive with lid open.

8 **Contact feeder.** Showing mesh hole before inverting.

5. Gloves

As a first year beekeeper you will probably be keen to wear gloves. Equipment suppliers have a range of light leather gauntlets for you to choose from. These will enable you to handle your frames but prevents stings to your hands. Some beekeepers like more feel and either do their inspections with bare hands or using thin medical latex gloves. As your confidence grows you may also wish to use your bare hands, but to start with I would suggest you wear leather gauntlets.

6. Bee brush

This is a long handled soft haired brush that helps you to move the bees from the edges of your brood box, crown board and roof when closing up your hive. It can also be used by a partner to remove any bees clinging to your bee suit when you have finished your inspection.

Feeders

There are a number of different types of feeders you can buy. Perhaps as you gain more experience you will wish to try them, however to start with the rapid or contact feeder will enable you to successfully feed your bees when they require it. Depending on your choice and size of feeder, you will need to place one or two empty supers on the crown board, to enable the hive roof to fit when a feeder is in place.

7. Rapid feeder

I personally prefer this method of feeding. The feeder fits over the crown board hole and you are able to see the bees climbing up the central aperture to collect the sugar solution and take down into the hive. To refill you only need to remove the hive roof, lift the feeder lid and you are able to see how much solution is left in the container. The feeder holds just over 2 litres (3.5 pints) of solution, so generally enough for a couple of days supply. I also find that this is the cleanest method, as by carefully refilling, it does not leave excess solution to make a sticky mess on the crown board.

8. Contact feeder

This feeder is basically a bucket with a lid and a small mesh covered opening. To use, you fill the bucket with the sugar solution, fix the lid and invert. Though some solution will drip out, a vacuum will be created to hold the remaining solution in. It is recommended that when you first invert it you do it well away from the hive. This prevents dripped sugar solution being close by and thus prevents robbing bees near your hive. The feeder is then placed over the hole in the crown board and the bees are able to collect the sugar solution through the mesh opening. The advantage of a contact feeder is that they come in three sizes: 1.0/2.5/4.5 litres (1/4, 1/2 and 1 gallon) capacity. So useful if you are not able to visit your hive daily to refill when you are feeding your bees.

All items can be bought through retail bee equipment suppliers either from their outlets or over the internet. As time progresses there will be other equipment you may wish to purchase, e.g. a honey extractor, but there is no need to rush into this outlay as your local association should have at least one extractor which will be available for hire for a small fee. The items listed are all the important ones when starting out.

Using your smoker

Your smoker is an essential piece of equipment and perhaps understanding what its purpose is, will help you in using it. Bees as wild creatures have an instinct as to what is happening around them. It is understood that colonies in forests, where wild fires can occur, are sensitive to smoke which sets off the bees instinctive alarm bell. With the first smell of smoke, bees will start taking in uncapped nectar and honey, known as engorgement. The bees collect their stores in the expectation that they may need to move home and fast. If the smoke becomes thicker, most of the bees will engorge themselves before taking flight. If it diminishes and the danger is over, the bees will return the nectar and honey back into the cells.

We as beekeepers smoke our bees to occupy them whilst we carry out our inspections. Some advocate smoking the entrance and then waiting a few minutes before opening the hive. Bees once they are engorged with honey are less likely to sting, hence our use of smoke. I personally do not smoke the entrance of my hives, as I have found it aggravates my bees unnecessarily. As a beginner and as you get to know the temperament of your bees, you only can judge this by the experience of how your bees react.

Before using your smoker for the first time, have a practice with it well away from your hive. Light it a few times, see how long your chosen fuel smoulders for. Basically get used to handling it. Once you are confident with it and start using it around a hive, you will find it so much easier to handle, especially if you don't have to keep relighting it.

Hints & tips

- Beware, should you ever need to relight your smoker, never do it with your veil covering your face. Many a beekeeper has had the painful experience, whilst blowing on their fuel through their veil, to find that the mesh veil has melted and the hot mesh has painfully stuck to their face.

When lighting your smoker, light a small piece of your chosen fuel and place it in the smoker. Add more fuel and tightly pack it in. Most beginners don't pack enough in and due to the amount of air in the smoker find their fuel burns too quickly. Your smoker needs to blow cool white smoke. If you find it is blowing sparks to begin with, wait a bit or add some long fresh grass on top of the fuel. You do not want to singe your bees. Once your hive is open, never blow smoke down into the hive. Firstly your bees will not like it and secondly if you do this into the supers where the honey is stored, you will blow in minute carbon deposits which will show up and taint your honey. To remove bees off the tops of the frames you only need a couple of puffs of smoke over them. I have found that I seldom do any smoking over the hive when starting my inspection. When closing the hive to enable me to refit supers, queen excluder and crown board I give the bees a puff or two, to encourage them off the edges so I don't crush them. Other than this I seldom need to use it, but always have it lit and at hand should I find for whatever reason my bees have become a little more agitated.

Once you have completed your inspection, twist and stuff some fresh long grass into the nozzle end. The lack of oxygen will soon extinguish your smoker. Your smoker will still be hot, so be aware. It has been known for beekeepers to place their smoker in their shed or the boot of their car, before shortly finding they are going up in flames. Also be careful where you tip the burnt cinders out of your smoker, a dry hedge or grassed ditch could easily catch light. If you set the ground alight near to your hives, you might experience what bees do in the wild, seeing them vacate the hives leaving them empty.

Above: First inspection of a hive two weeks after having hived a nucleus of bees.

Opposite: A couple of puffs of smoke and the bees will go down between the frames.

Hints & tips

- **Make certain your smoker is fully out and cool before putting it away**

Bees

"it's a hard life being a honey bee"

The honey bee that we as beekeepers keep is the European Honey Bee (Apis Mellifera) There are four main species of honey bee around the world, however, the European honey bee is the species that beekeepers generally keep in hives. This species is highly productive in the pollination of plants and in producing high quality honey for us to enjoy.

Within a hive there are three types of bees: Workers, drones and a queen. Each has its own specific position within the colony. It is a misconception that the queen is the ruler of the colony. The queen is just one part and the workers are not there to serve her, but to work together for the good of the colony. The queens' only task within the colony is to lay eggs, so that the workers can raise young and thus increase the number of bees. In a healthy colony at the height of summer, numbers within a hive can reach between 50,000 to 60,000 bees. All are workers, except for the one queen and up to 1500 drones.

Workers

These are the majority of bees in a hive and are all infertile females. After emerging from its cell, the immature young bee is set to work immediately. The first task in her life cycle is as a cleaner, preparing the empty cells ready for the queen to lay her eggs. Within a few days she is able to feed the larvae with pollen and nectar brought in by the older foraging bees. As her glands mature she is next able to cap the larvae and honey cells, plus build new comb within the hive. Two weeks into her life she will transfer pollen and nectar from the foraging bees and be able to store this food in the cells. Nearly mature and with her sting formed after 18 days of life, she will become an entrance guard. With her mandibles strong now, she will patrol the entrance to check returning foragers and to evict any intruder. Sniffing each bee, she will know if a bee from another colony is attempting to intrude her hive and if need be will kill the intruder with her sting. However, in doing so, she will die also. She will also at this time take her first short flights just outside the entrance of the hive. Three weeks into her life and fully mature, she becomes a forager. For the next three weeks she will collect nectar, pollen, propolis and water bringing it into the hive to pass on to her younger sisters to store. As a forager she has to survive the hazards outside the hive of other insects and birds and if successful she will have lived in total six weeks. Her three weeks as a forager will have seen her fly many miles carrying her own body weight in nectar and pollen and at this time after all her hard work she will die of exhaustion. If she is born

Honey bee collecting pollen from a quince flower.

in late autumn, she will live longer as most of her life will be spent clustered together throughout the winter. Come the first signs of spring though, she will be out foraging until exhausted.

Drones

During the summer months there are up to 1500 drones in a colony. Drones are male, larger in size and stingless. Their purpose within the colony is only to mate with a virgin queen. Within the hive all they do is eat and when looking for a queen to mate with will fly and mate on the wing. I have heard reports that drones and a queen will mate at heights of up to 5000 feet (1500 m) above the ground. Mating though is the end of his life as when he becomes unattached from the queen his sexual organs are ripped from his body and he dies in freefall. Naturally not all drones find a queen to mate with, as winter approaches the worker bees do not require an unproductive bee eating their food stocks, therefore the drones are forced from the colony and die from cold or starvation.

The queen

For the beekeeper the queen is very important for the laying of eggs to increase the size of the colony. The more worker bees within a hive, the greater the amount of honey is stored that we can later harvest. The queen is larger than all the other bees and can be spotted due to her elongated body and short wings. She likes to stay hidden in the darkness of a hive, so to aid spotting her most beekeepers mark her thorax with a coloured mark. You will soon be able to spot queen cells within your hive, these individual cells, looking like acorns, hang from the bottom or centre of a frame and generally will appear during April, May and June. Royal jelly secreted by the workers is fed to the larvae in a queen cell, once emerged she will fly within 3 days to mate. Mating in flight with up to 12 drones, she will have received enough sperm to last her egg laying life. Having mated she returns to the colony and starts her egg laying cycle. To lay an egg the queen backs into a freshly cleaned cell and attaches the tiny rice shaped egg to the back wall. At the height of her productivity she can lay up to 2000 eggs per day. Queens can live for 5-7 years, but it is accepted that by her third year she has started to decline in fertility. When she comes to the end of her productivity the worker bees sense this and will raise a new queen and on hatching the new virgin queen will take over from her mother. As beekeepers we require the queen to be as productive as possible and it is necessary at the end of her productivity to kill her, either by first allowing the workers to produce a new queen or to introduce a new queen to the colony.

From egg to bee

From an egg being laid by the queen it takes 3 days for the egg to hatch into a larva. On hatching, the young workers feed it royal jelly for another 3 days before feeding it a mixture of pollen and honey. As it grows it sheds its skin and curls up into a 'C' shape in the bottom of the cell. After 6 days it stops eating, now straight and filling the cell it is ready to be entombed. The workers cap the cell using a mixture of wax and propolis sealing the larva in. Over the next 12 days the larva pupates changing from a grub to an insect. On completion of this metamorphosis the young honey bee emerges from its cell. Capped drone cells are usually in a cluster along the top part of a frame. These areas of drone cells are easy to spot as the cells are larger and domed shape. A drone will emerge 24 days after the queen has laid the egg. Queens in their larger acorn sized cells develop more quickly taking just 16 days overall and as beekeepers we need to keep a special eye on queen cells to prevent the colony swarming.

Capped brood and cells with larvae waiting to be capped.

Capped drone cells - pronounced dome shape compared to capped worker bee cells.

A drone bee emerging from its capped cell.

Queen cells along the bottom of a frame.

Previous page: Honey bee collecting pollen from flowering Ivy.

Opposite: Honey bee collecting pollen from blossom on a sloe bush.

Above: A drone bee on a frame of brood.

Opposite: Bees on a frame of capped brood.

Propolis

Bees love their propolis, but for the beekeeper it gets everywhere. Propolis is a sticky resinous substance that bees collect from the bark and buds of trees. Generally orange/brown in colour the bees use it to seal gaps in the hive to stop draughts. As you will discover when opening your hive your bees like to seal these gaps and the frames. However, your hive tool will crack these seals for you to remove the frames and hive parts. It is also used as an antiseptic by the bees in the cell walls to prevent mould and infections. Bees will also mummify larger creatures which have died within the hive, but are too large to eject. Mummifying the carcass stops it decaying and makes it odourless and harmless to them. Propolis is also used in alternative medicines and is said to relieve various conditions including inflammation, viral diseases, ulcers and minor burns. It is also used as a varnish for delicate wood objects such as violins.

Royal jelly

Honey bees secrete royal jelly from their hypo pharyngeal glands and feed it to young larvae. It is only fed to them for a few days before feeding them pollen and nectar. If the colony wishes to produce a new queen, the queen larva is only fed royal jelly; this feeding develops her morphology to induce the development of ovaries which are needed for laying eggs. Royal Jelly is much sought after in medicine for its antibiotic character and is also used in some cosmetics.

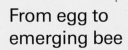

From egg to emerging bee

Workers - 21 days
Drones - 24 days
Queen - 16 days

Bee stings

As a beekeeper you will occasionally be stung, it is an occupational hazard. Naturally when doing inspections covering up will help prevent stings. I find you get stung when you are a little careless, nipping a bee and usually when you least expect it, especially when removing your bee suit having not seen one still clinging to you. Another time is doing a small job around the hive, when not covered. I had a period of time when I would get stung in my hair having removed the veil. I put this down to the shampoo I had been using. My wife had bought shampoo using natural products and I believe this may have had bee products in it, which attracted bees to my head. I have changed shampoo and the problem has gone away.

Bee stings affect people in different ways, some receive a mild irritation and others can have a serious allergic reaction. When a bee stings it leaves the stinger in the skin which continues to pump venom into us for up to 20 minutes, so try to remove the stinger as quickly as possible. The sting may be painful for a few hours with swelling and itching for up to a week. An ice pack or the use of an antihistamine in tablet or cream form may help, as will Piriton® tablets.

For anyone who has a serious allergic reaction they will need urgent medical attention. Symptoms of an allergic reaction can be a raised rash, headache, fever, severe swelling of the face, tongue and lips, possibly breathing difficulties and collapse. Anaphylatic shock is deadly serious so do not delay in calling the emergency services. Never be tempted to take someone suffering a severe reaction to hospital yourself, always call an ambulance and inform the operator that the problem relates to a bee sting.

Varroa mite

You may have first taken an interest in bees and bee keeping following the worldwide media coverage of the death of bee colonies due to the varroa mite. First discovered in south-east Asia in the early 1900's the varroa mite is now found globally except in Australia. This mite is a virulent parasite which lives on brood and bees, feeding off their bodily fluids; it carries viruses and can cause deformity in young bees. In extreme cases the mite will kill whole colonies. Varroa mite are reddish brown in colour approximately 1.2mm in size and though difficult to spot, can sometimes be seen clinging to the body of adult bees, though usually only when infections levels are high. A simpler method to spot any infestation in a hive is in the larvae, most notably in drone larvae.

Drone larvae are the preferred breeding site for the mite and for this reason many beekeepers remove excess drone brood larvae and inspect it to see if the mite is present. There are a number of chemical treatments beekeepers can use to control mite and hives have wire mesh floors to aid seeing dead or groomed mite which have fallen through on to the board. Seeing the occasional varroa mite, alive or dead in one of your hives is not a problem, if in the autumn you carry out your annual mite treatment. However, the mite are contagious and can easily be spread by drones or swarms, so should you see greater numbers, then it is paramount you speak to an expert beekeeper or report it to your local government bee inspector.

Much research is being carried out worldwide on the varroa mite and though it may not lead to it being eliminated it may in the future be controlled.

A varroa mite on the back of a honey bee.

Hints & tips

- Always put your veil on, however small a job you are doing around your hive

Where to place your hive

"don't upset the neighbours"

Before purchasing your hive, you need to think of where to place it. Careful consideration of this is important, as once your bees are in place you cannot move it within a 3 mile radius.

Bees are undoubtedly clever creatures, but if due consideration is not given, should you need to move the hive, the beekeeper can be responsible for the death of a sizeable proportion of the colony. Bees very soon know the exact location of their hive. Move a hive 10 metres or even turn the hive 180 degrees and the bees will not find the entrance and will therefore die. Should you ever need to move a hive, the hive needs to be relocated more than 3 miles away for a minimum of 2 weeks. Once these bees have established their new location, they can then again be relocated to your new choice of location.

Bees will generally live anywhere, but a little thought will help them, whether you are in a rural or urban location. Naturally closeness to pollen and nectar sources will assist, but bees are known to travel up to 5 miles in search of this. You have to think when choosing a location who else your bees might affect. So being too close to a neighbour's garden which they and their children regularly use is not the best place.

Placing your hive in a small garden is alright, it will help if you have a fence or high bush a few paces in front of the hive, as this will make the bees rise and descend quickly when leaving and returning to the hive. I was advised to have my bees in a position where they caught the early morning sun. Catching the eastern sunrise, warms the hive and the bees will therefore leave early in the day to start foraging. Bees like the sun and its warmth, however don't have the hive too exposed to direct sunshine during the hottest part of the day. Dappled shade at midday is perhaps the best

Hints & tips

- Choose your hive location carefully and try to stick with it

Beekeepers inspecting hives in a wood.

solution. Also think about what is above your hive, especially if placed on the edge of trees. On windy days a constant tapping from a branch will agitate your bees and major damage to the hive and colony could happen should a bow break and fall on to it. Many urban beekeepers keep their hives on the roof of buildings or on waste ground alongside rail tracks. These can be ideal locations as they are well away from other city dwellers. Before putting your hive in place, it pays to lay a few paving slabs. Ventilation of the hive is very important, so placing your hive on slabs will prevent grass and weeds growing under it and hindering the flow of air. I was concerned that my chosen spot for two of my hives was on the edge of a lawn, which I regularly cut with a tractor mower. At first I drove by quickly within a foot or two of the hive, but I have found they pay no attention to me or the lawn mower.

Perhaps your own garden or property is not an ideal location to keep bees. Farmers, horticulturists or allotment gardeners rely on bees to pollinate their crops. Many would be only too pleased to have bees on their land. So if you are

struggling for a location on your own property, ask around, you will probably find someone to help you locate your hives. Your local association may also have a list of property owners who have offered their land for hives to be placed on. An ideal location is anyone with an orchard; apple, cherry, plum and pear are all great sources of pollen for your bees when they are in blossom and fruit growers need pollination to get a good harvest. Commercial beekeepers around the world transfer their hives to pollen sources throughout a season; examples of this in Britain is transferring them to the moors when heather is in flower and in the USA transferring them from almond orchards to orange groves.

One place probably not wise to place your hives is where there is public access. Unfortunately there are idiots who take pleasure in throwing rocks and the like in an attempt to knock over a hive. There have also been reports of hives being stolen, so when looking for a location, try not to choose a place where they are too visible from the road or where the general public have too easy access.

Opposite: A tractor lawn mower passing close by hives in a garden.

Above: A bee hive in a garden in spring with daffodils in flower.

Hints & tips

- Place hives on solid slabs to aid ventilation

Orchards are a good location for hives for the bees to pollinate the fruit trees.

Getting & transferring your bees

"where do I get them"

Having got your required equipment together, the next thing is where to get your first bees. There are three possible solutions - a nucleus of bees, a colony or the collection of a swarm.

As a first year beekeeper the best option is a nucleus, as taking a full colony or capturing a swarm might be overly daunting. Initially I started with three hives, two of which were started from a nucleus. A nucleus is really a half colony, consisting of 5 to 6 frames of bees, brood, eggs and larvae with a queen. Basically it is a box, with air vents and an entrance hole, in which the frames sit. A nucleus of bees can be purchased from most bee equipment retailers or local beekeepers. Your local association will know which of their members will have nucleuses to sell. Nucleuses are generally for sale from May and throughout the summer. However earlier ones will have a previous years queen whereas later ones should have a current year queen and will only become available once the newly reared virgin queen has mated.

Having arranged where your first nucleus is coming from, be prepared well in advance of it arriving. You will be given an approximate date, but this is flexible due to when the virgin queens mate. Once you get the call that it is ready, you may be required to go and collect it or it may be delivered. It is best to get it in the evening after any foraging bees have returned for the night. Before receiving it have your hive stand in place in your chosen position for the hive.

Hints & tips

- Ask your local association for members who sell nucleuses of bees.

A nucleus box in place on a hive stand.

On arriving home with the nucleus, place the nucleus box on the hive stand and open the entrance hole. The bees might sound a bit agitated, but this is normal as they have travelled in a sealed box. Leave the box for a minimum of 24 hours and the bees will settle and the following morning the foraging bees will start to exit the nucleus to get their bearings in their new location.

When you are ready to transfer your nucleus into your hive, light your smoker, put on your bee suit, have your hive tool in hand, an empty super and a feeder with some 1:1 sugar solution ready, (see page 67 for sugar solution measurements). Lift the nucleus box off the hive stand and stand beside it. On top of the hive stand put

in place the wire mesh floor with an entrance block and an empty brood box. If your nucleus is of five frames and your brood box will in total take eleven frames, place 3 frames of new wax foundation at the furthest point of the hive away from you. Open the lid of the nucleus and give a little smoke over the tops of the frames. Remove the first frame with bees on. It may be stuck down with propolis, but your hive tool will easily dislodge it. Place the first frame in your hive next to a frame of foundation. Continue lifting out and placing the frames in your hive, placing them in exactly the same order that they were in the nucleus. These frames will end up being central in your hive. You should now have 5 frames of bees and 3 frames of foundation.

With your hive tool gently nudge the frames together, so that they fit across the hive from the far end. Nearest to you will be a gap, where you place three more frames of wax foundation and finally fit your dummy board. You will now see your brood box is full of frames all parallel to each with the five frames from the nucleus central in your hive. When you are happy that all the frames are in place, check the inside of the nucleus box as many bees will still be clinging on. Lift the nucleus box over the hive and with a shake or two dislodge these bees on to the tops of the frames. Many will fall, but not all. To get the rest into the hive, place the box against the hive entrance and as evening falls the remaining bees will find their way into the hive to join the others. Close the hive giving a few puffs of smoke over the tops of the frames to encourage the bees to go down into the hive, then place the crown board with the holes covered, diagonally on top of the brood box and wiggle it into place to dislodge any bees, so you do not crush any. To give the bees some feed, wait until evening so

as not to excite the bees and also invite robbing bees. Uncover one of the holes on the crown board and place your feeder over it. Fill the feeder with the 1:1 sugar solution. So your bees know that feed is there, it pays to drip a little of the sugar solution on to the frames, through the feeder hole. Once this is completed, cover the feeder. With the feeder in place, the roof will now not fit due to the height of the feeder, so you have to place an empty super on top before replacing the roof. To avoid trapping bees in the roof, give them a bit of smoke or use your bee brush to wipe them away then fit the roof. You now have your first colony of bees.

Depending on the weather conditions, you will need to keep a daily eye on the feed. If conditions are warm the bees will be out foraging, so the feeder will only be needed for a few days. Keep topping up the feeder, if the bees have had enough, they will stop taking it down. When they have stopped taking the sugar solution the feeder and empty super can then be removed.

Above: Bees soon know the location of their new home.

Opposite: Transfering frames of bees from a nucleus.

Opening the hive

"your first inspection"

You have had your nucleus of bees for two weeks now and it is time to do your first hive inspection. As a new beekeeper you will be itching to do your first inspection, but be patient and give them this period of time to settle in.

Within a day of hiving your bees you will see bees in-flight around the hive and foraging bees returning with pollen on their legs. If this is the case, then the queen is laying eggs to produce young and therefore increasing the size of the colony.

Choose a fine day for your inspection and if you can, try to do it near the middle of the day, when many of the foraging bees will be out. Put your bee suit on and before pulling up the veil and zipping it in place, light the smoker and ensure it is smoking well. Once you have all you need with you and are covered up, you can if you wish give the hive entrance a few puffs of smoke. Wait a couple of minutes after smoking the entrance and now you can remove the roof, laying it alongside the hive, with the top of the roof to the ground. Having it in this position gives you an area to place frames in as you work. Using your hive tool run the sharp end round the crown board cracking the propolis that the bees have deposited. Sometimes it can be quiet hard to get the crown board to release and other times it comes away easily. Once free, lift off the crown board and inspect the underside, you will

see bees clinging to it, but what you are checking for is that the queen is not here. It is unlikely, but better to be safe as you do not want her to drop on to the ground. Now place the crown board on the ground leaning against the entrance to the hive.

You will see the open hive now with the frames lined up across the width of the hive. Some bees will be flying but there should not be too many bees airborne around you. You will see bees on the frame top bars, so to keep them occupied you can give a few puffs of smoke across the tops of the frames. Do not try blowing the smoke down into the hive as it only needs a few puffs over the top. Stand to the side of your hive with the frames going away from you and using your hive tool gently remove the dummy board. This should be the closest frame to you. Again check for the queen and stand this in the roof, in a position which matches the layout of your hive. Now you are going to remove the first frame, lever it out

Opposite top: Lifting off the crown board.

Opposite below: A few puffs of smoke over the tops of the frames.

and as this is your first inspection, you should see just a frame of wax foundation. Place this alongside the dummy board in the hive roof. Next remove the following frame, this should be similar or you may see that some of the wax foundation has been drawn out and the bees have made a start creating their comb. Place this in the roof also. Do not worry about the few bees on these frames, they will find their way back.

The reason for placing a few frames in the roof is to give yourself working space as you go through each frame in the hive. You can now work through each frame lifting it out to inspect. The further you go into the hive the more bees you will find covering the frames. To help you see the comb better it helps to remove some of these bees. Holding each end of the frame and holding it over and slightly in the gap you have removed it from, give it a firm downward shake once or twice. This will dislodge many of the bees and they will fall, totally unharmed into the bottom of the hive. Having done this, you may find your bees are now a bit more agitated, if so, give them a few more puffs of smoke over the hive and this should calm them down. It is always handy to have a cloth ready should you at anytime feel your bees are a bit too agitated or if you feel uncomfortable. If this is the case, cover the hive with the cloth and walk away. They will soon settle down and you can then return to complete your inspection.

Continue your inspection, checking the next frame placing it back in the hive against the outer wall nearest to you. You will see that now you have created a space in the hive which makes it much easier for you to handle each individual frame. You will now have reached the frames you placed in the hive from your nucleus. Inspect each one shaking off the bees and you should be able to spot eggs and larvae. To spot them it helps if you can place the sun over your shoulder to aid in lighting the inside of the cells. Keep going through all the frames and you should be able to spot pollen and nectar cells and as you reach the central frames, the sealed brood. You will also notice generally along the top portion of the frame stored honey which has been capped with a white creamy coloured wax.

Hints & tips

- Do not stand in front of the hive blocking the flight path - your bees won't like it

- Check each frame to see if you can spot the queen

- Hold frames over the hive, if heavy you can rest a corner on another frame bar

Opposite: Placing the crown board against the front of the hive.

Above right: Lifting our a frame to inspect it for brood and eggs.

Do not worry if you do not spot the queen, she will be busy laying eggs and tends to hide away from the light. Most purchased nucleuses of bees will have the queen marked. This is a coloured ink mark on her thorax and is often colour coded to indicate the year she was hatched. If you do spot her, you will see that she is larger and definitely stands out from the crowd. The reason for your first inspection is to check that the queen is laying, so if you are able to see eggs, larvae and sealed brood then all is well. Having gone through all the frames, you can now ease them back into their original position, until you have a space nearest to you, where the two frames and dummy board were

removed. Replace the frames you placed in the roof, in the same position and orientation as they were and then add the dummy board. With all the frames back in the hive you can nudge them into place using your hive tool and you are ready to close up the hive. Give the edges of the hive a quick smoke to remove any bees and place the crown board at an angle across the top of the hive. Then gently wiggle the crown board into place. Occasionally you will crush the odd bee but doing this will help you from crushing too many. Make certain the crown board holes are covered, clear the top of any bees with a bit of smoke and put the roof on. You have now completed your first inspection.

Keeping notes

It is a good idea to keep notes of each of your hives. I keep a card in the roof of each hive which enables me to make quick written notes after each inspection. I then keep more comprehensive notes taken from the cards entering the details into a spread sheet on my computer. Keeping notes will give you a history of the hive and its activities and your actions over the years.

A good example of this for me was seeing an unmarked queen in one of my hives at the beginning of the season. I marked her with a dab of white marker, but was certain when I had seen the queen the season before that she was marked green. By going back through my notes, I was able to see that I was correct and therefore the colony either late in the season the previous year or early in the current season had superseded her. Making notes of the numbers of sides of brood and honey stores will enable you to actively gauge how strong or weak a colony is, plus knowing exact dates when honey was extracted or medication had been given to treat for varroa, as examples.

Hive Card

Hive No. 3

Date	Notes
23° March 2010	4 sides brood Condition excellent - Spring Clean
11th April 2010	12 sides brood - 1st Drone cells Condition excellent
17th April 2010	14 sides brood Added ½ brood box + super
23° April 2010	17 sides brood - marked Queen/white Honey in super - none capped Excellent condition
30° April 2010	18 + 10 sides brood Queen cell larva frame 9 12 + sides honey uncapped
15th May 2010	Created Artificial Swarm New Hive No. 5

Opposite: First inspection. Frames from the nucleus can be seen central in the hive.

Above: Frame showing empty cells awaiting an egg, uncapped larvae and sealed honey at the top of the frame.

Above: Frame showing cells with different coloured pollen, stored nectar cells and sealed honey.

Above: Frame showing sealed brood.

Above: Close up of larvae cells. Larvae can be seen curled up in the cells.

Queen marking

Marking the queen will help you in locating her within the brood box, especially when it comes to splitting a hive to prevent swarming. There are a number of tools to aid in capturing or holding her whilst you mark her. I use a queen cage, which is placed over her and carefully pressed into the comb. Worker bees can escape through the spiked cage. Gently pressing down, being careful not to crush her will enable you to place a coloured mark on her thorax, using a special marker pen which is available in a variety of colours from bee equipment suppliers. As a hobby beekeeper I mark all my queens with a white marker, as I find white stands out better. Commercial beekeepers will use colour coded markers to enable them to identify the year that a queen was hatched.

Above: A queen cage.

Opposite: A marked queen stands out amongst the other bees.

Queen yearly colour codes

Year Ending	Colour
1 or 6	White
2 or 7	Yellow
3 or 8	Red
4 or 9	Green
5 or 0	Blue

Feeding bees

"if you take their honey you have to return something"

Bees are intelligent creatures and know they have to store food to survive the winter months. However, as beekeepers we remove some of their winter stores of honey and need to substitute it. We also can help them by supplementing their feed in harsh times, as and when they require it. Knowing how and when to feed your bees is very important in maintaining a strong colony.

Spring feed

At the first signs of spring, your bees will be out foraging for the first pollen and nectar of the year. As these first supplies come in, the bees natural instinct is to increase the size of the colony and the queen will start laying eggs. However, your bees stock of food within the hive will be at its lowest and this is now the time you may need to help the colony. Having survived winter, you do not want them to die due to the lack of food. If you feel food stocks are low, prepare a 2:1 sugar solution and give to the bees by rapid or contact feeder, (see page 67 for sugar solution measurements). You may have to keep topping up the feeder for a couple of weeks until nectar is in full flow. You can't give them too much, so once they have taken all they require they will stop taking it down and you can remove the feeder.

Spring can be a dangerous time for the colony in temperate climates. Spring can arrive for a few days and very quickly revert back to cold and wet weather. Your bees think that spring has arrived and have started collecting pollen and nectar to feed the new larvae. A cold spell will halt new flower growth and without being able to forage the bees stock of food dwindles further. Again this is the time to add a feeder and give them a strong 2:1 sugar solution to see them through this period. As a beekeeper it is your hive management and observation skills which are needed at this time of year. Regular hefting of the hives, observing bee movements and the weather, will all help you to determine whether they need feeding. If uncertain, feed them as they will only take the feed should they need it.

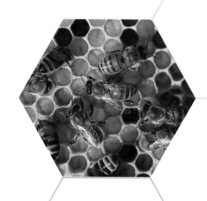

A rapid feeder on a hive. Bees can be seen in the central aperture collecting the sugar solution.

Feeding a nucleus or swarm

If you have taken delivery of a nucleus of bees or have managed to collect a swarm, feeding will help to get them started and settled in your hive. Once transferred to a hive, a nucleus has very little feed on the frames and a swarm will go into a new hive without any honey stores. Your hive will have frames of new wax foundation, so to assist the bees in drawing out this foundation to create their own comb, we as beekeepers can give them some help. Prepare a 1:1 sugar solution and feed the hive. As with other feeding, they will take only what they require and as soon as they have what they need they will stop taking it.

Autumn feed

Having harvested the honey from the supers and given the hive its Varroa mite treatment, now is the time to feed the colony, so that they have plenty of food stores throughout the winter. This feeding needs to take place whilst it is still relatively warm (15°C - 59f) so that the bees can evaporate the water content to enable them to store it. It is recommended that each hive will require a minimum of 13.5 kg (30 lbs) of winter stores.

Above: Snowdrops. One of the first pollen sources after winter.

Opposite: Honey bee collecting moisture from plant leaves in a garden pond.

Prepare a 2:1 sugar solution and feed the hive with a Rapid or Contact feeder. You will be surprised how much and how quickly the bees will take this solution, but keep feeding them until they stop taking it. As you make your final inspection before winter, you need to see that the frames are full of stores. As with honey, the bees will cap the stored cells with a white wax and it will look the same as stored honey. I have found that I only give each of my hives about 7 kg (15lbs) of solution, as my bees have an abundance of ivy pollen and nectar to collect close by in the autumn and they have used this to build up their stores. You might find that in your location there are also plenty of late flowering plants such as ivy and they will use these to build up their stocks. You have to use your own judgement and from your inspections will be able to judge when the colony has ample food stocks. Once you are satisfied that the required stores are in place, the feeder can be removed and you can make your final winter preparations.

Winter feed

Half way through the winter, you need to check that the colony's supply of food has not reduced down too much. Hefting the hive will give you a good indication; you can supplement this should you feel that food stocks are running low. Fondant icing sugar is available from bee equipment suppliers or you can get packs of it from your local supermarket. When feeding your bees fondant, try and wait for a relatively warmer day, hopefully with some sun on the hive. You need to work quickly, as opening the hive releases the heat the colony has created when clustered together. Place the fondant package directly on to the frames over the cluster, adding an eke for spacing and closing the hive again. This should take you no more than 30 seconds. You can check the fondant in a month's time and replenish if it has been eaten.

Water

One area which is often overlooked is that bees need a supply of drinking water. I am lucky enough to have a water filled ditch close to my hives, but any source within 10 meters will do. However, in dry periods my source of water can dry up, so I have placed a rectangular plastic garden pot close by. As bees cannot swim it is essential that you give them a floating platform to land on whilst they take in water. Twigs or leaves floating on the surface will suffice. I tried wine bottle corks, but the squirrels very quickly discovered them and removed them to their hides. Bees prefer stagnant water, so don't worry if the water does not look too appetizing to us.

Sugar solution measurements

- **1:1 Sugar Solution**   1lb sugar / 1 pint water
  0.5kg sugar / 0.5 litres water

- **2:1 Sugar Solution**   2lb sugar / 1 pint water
  1kg sugar / 0.5 litres water

1kg = 2.2 lb		1 litre = 0.76 pint	
2kg = 4.4 lb		2 litres = 3.52 pint	
5kg = 11 lb		5 litres = 8.80 pint	
10kg = 22 lb		10 litres = 17.6 pint	
1lb = 0.5 kg		1 pint = 0.568 litres	
2lb = 0.9 kg		2 pints = 1.136 litres	
5lb = 2.3 kg		5 pints = 2.84 litres	
10lb = 4.5 kg		10 pints = 5.68 litres	

See page 76 for detailed instructions.

Subsequent inspections

"adding supers"

Regular inspections of your hives are necessary for the welfare of your bees. During spring you should be inspecting your hives every 7 to 9 days. Generally you are checking your hive to see if the queen is laying eggs successfully and that your bees are not running out of space.

Also during this period, queen cells can be found and you may need to take preventative measures to stop the colony swarming. In the summer after the swarming period, inspections can be less frequent as long as you have allowed for the colony numbers to expand with supers in place.

Following the same procedure as with your first inspection, you need to go through each frame. As time progresses you will see that all the frames are drawn out and the comb the bees have built are filled either with eggs, larvae or capped brood. Other frames will have cells full of pollen and nectar, some capped and others waiting to be capped. In the top portion of the frames you will also see sealed honey.

You will also need to be checking for queen cells, if you have taken delivery of your nucleus of bees late in the season then you are unlikely to see queen cells hanging from the bottom of the

frames. Those who received their nucleus earlier, could see them appearing. If this is the case, in your first year, should you see queen cells it is advisable to crush them or cut them out, as you don't want your colony to produce a new queen and swarm.

If you have received your nucleus from a reputable supplier, you should find them clean of any varroa mite or other bee diseases. But you need to keep an eye open whilst going through your hive frame by frame. It is highly unlikely, but check to see if you have any varroa mite clinging to the backs of any bees. If you see one or two it is not a problem, but more and it would be best to get advice from an experienced beekeeper, as you might need to treat them immediately to stop the mite increasing. Also check the mite board under the wire mesh floor for as the bees clean the hive, debris will fall through. Look to see if you can see any dead mite. Look also for Chalk brood, this is

Previous page: A selection of flowers your bees will be attracted to.

Opposite: A National hive with one super in place.

a fungal disease, the fungal spores are ingested by the larvae and germinate in the gut thus killing it. The larvae are mummified and look like a cell filled with chalk. The house bees will eject these from the hive, but should you see the occasional one, you can help by removing it. Chalk brood is seasonal and seldom a problem, but if you see more than the odd one or two, speak to an experienced beekeeper. One other problem which first year beekeepers might encounter is wax moth. Again you are unlikely to see a major infestation, but remove the occasional one you might see. To spot, it is likely you will see a silk trail over the sealed brood, smaller but similar to that left by a garden snail. A tip I was given to find the wax moth larva should you see any silk trails was to tap the frame with your hive tool a few times. This encourages the larva to appear from the cell allowing you to pinch it out. All these are unlikely to be a major problem in your first year. However, it is better if you are aware of these potential problems should they occur in the future.

At this stage in your beekeeping the most important check is to make certain your bees have plenty of space. If the weather has been favourable, the queen will have been laying constantly and these new eggs will hatch in 21 days, so the colony will be expanding rapidly. The colony needs space for the queen to lay her eggs and to store pollen and nectar, so we as beekeepers want to encourage the bees to expand and store honey for us to harvest. Once you see that the outer frames have had their wax foundation drawn out, now is the time to give them the extra space. You cannot do it too early, so it is better to create this extra space rather than later. To give your bees more space you need to add a super above the brood box. Adding a super is a simple and quick process. With the hive open, place a queen excluder on to the brood box. A puff of smoke over the top will clear the bees as you sit the queen excluder on top, with the slots at right angles to the frames. On top of this you add a super with the frames full of wax foundation and placed in the same direction as those in the brood box. The crown board is then replaced on to the super followed by the roof.

The bees will soon discover this extra space and will move up through the queen excluder, drawing out the wax foundation and creating comb for them to store honey in. With the queen excluder in place only worker bees can enter and return from the super, so the laying queen will have further space to lay in, as the food stores can now be placed above.

During the height of the pollen and nectar season, a strong colony can fill a super within a week. Keep a close eye on your hive, adding further supers as they are required. It is not unheard of for a hive to have four or five supers in place by the end of the season. If you are going to be away, so missing a weekly inspection, adding two supers at once will safe guard any rapid expansion whilst you are away.

This method of adding new supers on top of each other is known as Top Supering. Some beekeepers prefer Bottom Supering which is to add any new supers below the supers in place. This creates more work as you have to lift off the supers in place to add new ones below. However, some believe that this method encourages more honey to be stored as the bees have to travel less distance through the hive in order to store their honey. Both systems work and it is down to you which method you prefer.

I found with one of my hives, that the queen was laying eggs so rapidly that space for brood was running out within the brood box. If you find this, you can increase the size of the brood box, by placing a super on it, but without a queen excluder between it. The queen excluder can then be placed on top of the super, before adding further supers. By doing this you are basically creating one and half brood boxes and therefore giving ample space for the queen to lay her eggs in.

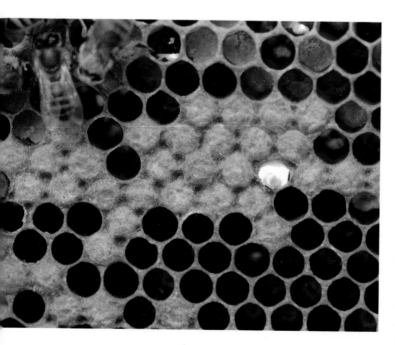

Hints & tips

- A Golden Rule – If you see bees on 6 to 7 frames in a super add another one

- Top super in the spring to allow space, bottom super in the summer to get honey

Left: An example of sealed brood with one cell of chalk brood.

Opposite: Commercial Beekeeper inspecting hives alongside Oil Seed Rape.

Wintering your bees

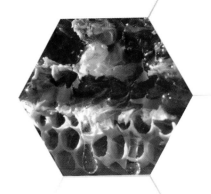

"give them a little help"

Having nurtured your bees through summer the preparation for the winter months is very important if they are to survive into the spring. At the end of August or early September you must start preparing your bees for winter.

Having harvested the honey now is the time to treat and protect against the varroa mite. A number of veterinary approved treatments can be purchased from bee equipment suppliers. The one I have used being a thymol based treatment under the trade name of Apiguard. If this is your chosen method, two 50g trays per hive will be required. Place one tray opened on to the brood frames in a corner of your hive for 10 to 14 days. You will find with the trays in place you cannot replace the crown board so this is when you would use an eke as a spacer, or if you don't have one, use an empty super instead. On inspecting the hive after this time, you should find that the gel has been taken down into the hive by the bees. Replace this tray with a new one and leave for the same period. This treatment is to keep the level of infestation to a minimum and should be applied primarily at the end of the summer, but can be applied at other times in the season as appropriate and provided supers storing honey are not in use. Always read the manufacturers guidelines for any chemical treatments you apply to your hives.

Left: Apiguard tray on frames in the hive.

Opposite: A Hive in the garden with snow falling.

Once the Varroa treatment has been applied now is the time to feed your bees. This enables them to build up a stock of food to last them through the winter. This is required to be done immediately as the outside temperature needs to still be warm (over 15°C – 59F) enough to enable the bees to reduce the water content to allow them to store the sugar in the comb cells. You will need to mix a 2:1 sugar solution. I purchased a large jam making pot which I found to be ideal to dilute the sugar granules into the syrup solution. Measuring two sugar to one of warm water, I slowly heat the sugar, stirring regularly until all the sugar has been diluted. Allow it to cool before funnelling into 2 litre plastic lemonade or cola bottles. I use these as they are ideal for pouring the sugar solution into the feeder when it is in place on the hive.

To feed your bees, you only have to remove the roof and open one of the holes in your crown board, placing the feeder over this hole. Once in place fill the feeder with the sugar solution and drip a little solution through the hole on to the frames to let the bees know that there is feed for them. Replace the feeder cover, add an empty super as a spacer and replace the hive roof. You will find that you will need to check the level of sugar solution daily or every other day, as you will be surprised how much and how quickly the bees will take it down. When refilling your rapid feeder, you will see the bees in the central aperture feeding on the solution. Slowly pour the sugar syrup into the feeder, so you do not drown the bees as the syrup level rises. The bees will move as you refill. However some will get immersed in it and you will think they will have drowned. Bees have a system to create an air pocket round them. This silver lining is visible and if not too deep into the syrup solution, they will slowly rise and extract themselves. You may also at times find the sugar solution has crystallized, preventing the bees getting to the

syrup. If you find this, remove the feeder, cover the hole in the crown board and wash the feeder in hot water. You can then replace it and refill with the sugar solution.

Your bees will need plenty of food to survive the winter, so continue feeding them; once they have all that they require they will stop taking any more of the solution down. A minimum of 13.5kg (30 pounds) of stored honey is the recommended amount necessary for a colony to survive winter. To give yourself a good indication of how much food is in the hive, try lifting a corner of the hive off the ground (hefting). If when attempting this, the hive feels that it is nailed to the ground, it is a good indication that the hive is full of food. Hefting is also a good method to judge how much food is still in the hive throughout the winter months. If the hive becomes light, then you will know that food is getting short and may need your attention.

Often at the end of August and during September, you will see many wasps attracted to your hives. As ripe fruit falls from trees, wasps seem to be in abundance as they gorge themselves. I have seen wasps attempting to gain entry into my hives and seen them attacked by the entrance guards. You can purchase glass wasp catching jars very cheaply, or even use an old jar with a small amount of orange juice or jam in it. I place a wasp jar on each hive and over this period catch hundreds of wasps. This

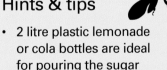

Hints & tips

- 2 litre plastic lemonade or cola bottles are ideal for pouring the sugar solution into the feeder

A hive with wire netting and strapped down during winter.

is far preferable than robbing wasps entering the hive and stealing stores.

With your feeding complete, there are a few more jobs you need to carry out. First remove the mite board below the wire mesh floor. This will allow fresh air to circulate throughout the hive and can remain off for winter. To allow further ventilation, uncover the holes on your crown board and cover with a tight wire mesh or as I have done, loosely cover the holes with hessian sacking. Bees can withstand the cold when clustered together, but a build up of moisture can cause problems, so by doing this it helps keep the hive well ventilated. The entrance to the hive needs reducing and many beekeepers fit a mouse guard. In cold winters, mice will find your hive a comfortable home, so the guard prevents them entering through the narrow holes. Experts have recently said that mouse guards are not necessary, as a standard restricted entrance block is small enough to prevent small rodents entering.

If your hives are in an open windy location or near large trees as mine are, place ratchet straps around them, so in the event of high winds or something falling on to a hive, the straps will keep the hive parts together. Another problem should we have a long period of frosty weather is woodpeckers. If they are unable to feed themselves, a hive is an attractive alternative and it is known for a woodpecker to create a large hole in the wall of a hive eating the bees. To prevent this I encase each hive in garden wire netting, just pinning it into place. Depending where you live, you may have other predators which might show an interest in your hives, if so it is best to seek local advice on the best way to protect them. Having completed these tasks you can now leave your bees in peace throughout the winter months.

Having completed your winter preparations in September and early October, clean and store

your equipment away in a dry place. Your supers, drawn frames and queen excluders can be scraped with your hive tool to remove excess wax and propolis. Wax moth can be attracted to your stored frames, so it is advisable to take steps to prevent this. I was advised to place the supers on blocks to aid ventilation and as you stack your supers on top of each other, place a sheet of newspaper between each one and drip some lavender oil on to it. I understand that the scent of lavender will keep wax moth at bay. To prevent mice getting in, place a queen excluder below the lowest and on top of the highest super.

The colony over winter will have been reduced down to about 10,000 bees, the drones will have been ejected and only the late hatched bees will be in the hive with the queen. Clustered together they will maintain the hive temperature seeing out the winter months. Keep a general eye on your hives though during winter, especially after strong winds or heavy rain. You might find on a warmer sunny day that some bees are out stretching their wings. It is a welcome sight to see them flying around the entrance knowing that chances are they are surviving the winter well. Don't be alarmed if on a sunny day you see a few dead bees on the landing board or outside the hive. Some bees will die during the winter months and as bees like to keep their home clean, they will dispose of any dead bees when it is warm enough for them to do so. The next day they will have all disappeared as the birds in your garden will be happy to receive this free meal.

Monthly you will need to check that the feed stores are holding out through the winter months. A quick visit to your hives and hefting will tell you by their weight how much food is still in the hive. By February stores may be starting to deplete and a little help from you might be necessary. If this is the case and if you can find a reasonably warm day with some sunshine

Hessian covering holes on the crown board.

Feeding the bees fondant. Placing it on the frames. NB Notice Eke in place.

Supers and nucleus boxes stored away for winter.

Dead bees outside the hive on a sunny day in February.

on your hive, you can give them a feed of fondant. Fondant icing, used to ice cakes, can be found in all supermarkets. Wrap the fondant package in cling film, to prevent it drying out too quickly and cut a strip out of one side of the packaging. Remove the hive roof and crown board placing the fondant with the cut hole side down, on to the frames where there is the largest concentration of bees. Work quickly, as you want to complete this task without losing too much of the heat from the hive. Once in place, you will need to fit an eke before fitting the crown board and roof. This high concentrated sugar feed will help the bees to survive until spring. However check regularly to see if they need more, feeding them as required until spring arrives and you see the bees bringing in new nectar and pollen.

Strong healthy colonies are those prepared well in spring and autumn.

Collecting swarms

"a free colony"

Many of you at this stage in your beekeeping may have no intention of going anywhere near a swarm of bees. However, if you are either brave or stupid or probably like me, a bit of both, then a swarm is an excellent way to get yourself a free colony.

Above: Bees swarming and starting to cluster on the trunk of an apple tree.

Opposite: Hiving a swarm, using a white sheet and ramp to enable bees to climb up into the hive.

As I wrote early in the book, I started with 3 hives, two of which came from nucleuses. My third hive I was able to colonise with a swarm which I collected. Collecting and hiving a swarm the first few times is stressful, exciting and every beekeeper if they get the opportunity, even if not actively involved in the collection should see this spectacle.

It is in the nature of bees to swarm. Some do have more of a tendency than others, but one of the trigger factors is a lack of space. As beekeepers we work towards swarm prevention, as losing half your colony will reduce the amount of honey you will harvest later in the year. However, there are occasions and it happens to the most experienced beekeepers, that a swarm is lost. Not particularly good news if it is your hive that has swarmed, but handy for the person who has the opportunity to collect it.

When bees are preparing to swarm, usually during May, June and into July, they engorge into themselves three days worth of honey stores. It is one of nature's spectacles to see thousands of bees departing a hive or their nest in the wild. It is as if a tap had been opened with bees pouring out and filling the sky. The sound of thousands of buzzing bees airborne looking for a place to settle is intimidating and unless covered, best to keep your distance. Soon after leaving their home, the bees will settle as a large cluster on a branch, a gate post or even on a piece of machinery. Often this cluster will resemble in shape a large rugby ball and is usually within 50 meters of their original home. Once they have clustered together, surrounding the queen, the scouts will be out

searching for a new home. This can take from one hour to three days. Once a new home has been found the colony will fly again and enter their new home to continue their breeding cycle.

Collecting a swarm can only be done when it is in a cluster and in an accessible position. Don't attempt to collect one if its position is going to put you in any danger, it is not worth the risk. If you are interested in colonising one of your hives, you will need to put the word out that you are interested in a swarm. I had spoken to a commercial gardener and he was able to telephone me having had swarms on two properties where he was working. Anyone who spots a swarm will have to call you and you

Nucleus box tied above swarm cluster
and smoking the bees into the box.

will have to drop everything, as they could soon
move on. If you are aiming to collect a swarm,
have all that you need ready in advance, so you
can quickly put it in your car and be off at a
moment's notice. The crucial items you will
need are: A skep or good size cardboard box (12
bottle wine box is ideal) with the bottom securely
taped, a white sheet, secateurs, your smoker and
protective clothing.

My first swarm was a small colony some 15 feet
high on the outside eave of a bungalow. I think
they had been there a while as they had built
some comb. I was successful in cutting them
down and getting them into a nucleus box and
then hiving them. Unfortunately after two days

'A swarm in May
is worth a load of hay;

a swarm in June
is worth a silver spoon;

but a swarm in July
is not worth a fly'

For it is then too late,
to store up honey before
the flowers begin to fade.

Wild Life in Southern County
R. Jefferies 1879

they left the hive. I was later to find out that this was probably due to me not immediately putting a feeder on, to help them draw out the wax foundation in the frames. I had learnt a lot though even if not entirely successful and was now more prepared should I get another call.

Fortunately this came 2 weeks later. My friendly gardener, called to say he was working in a garden preparing for a wedding where the reception was being held in a marquee. Naturally the bride and family were very concerned that they had thousands of bees flying about and didn't want this to happen during the reception. By the time I arrived the bees had disappeared, no sight or sound of them. We searched the garden and eventually found them about 10 feet up clustered in a large laurel bush. They were very calm and as I hoped, accessible. This time I had brought a hive with me and was glad I had as the colony would not have fitted into a nucleus box.

I positioned the hive on the grass, about 10 paces from the swarm. In place was the hive stand on short legs, brood box with frames, crown board and a roof. I laid a piece of board from the ground to the entrance of the hive and covered this with a white sheet. My aim was to get the swarm on to the sheet and as I had researched the bees would follow the queen into the hive. With the hive ready, I lit my smoker and dressed in my bee suit. Fortunately I had brought my wife's suit with me which I gave to the gardener. We discussed our plan of action on how we were going to collect the swarm and with this plan and beating hearts we put it into action. I had decided against smoking the cluster as I felt this might agitate them. Firstly we cut out a few of the lower branches to give us working room and easier access to them.

The bees were clustered mainly on one vertical branch and another less thick one.

We decided I would stand on a step ladder holding the main branch whilst the gardener slowly, without too much vibration, sawed through the branch lower down. Nervously I hung on expecting a cloud of bees to suddenly explode into the air. Once he had cut half way through the branch, he passed me some branch loppers and I carefully cut the thinner branch which was in part holding the cluster. As this was cut it held its position, not falling and taking bees with it. Our concern was that once the main branch was cut through, I would not be able to keep it vertical and it would fall sideways. Luckily with the final cut, I was able to hold it and was surprised that branch and cluster of bees was not heavier. Now having hold of it, I slowly made my way down the step ladder and carried the branch, still vertical towards the hive.

At this point I had about ten members of the wedding party watching my every move. I suggested they retreated a bit further as soon there would be lot of agitated bees in the air. Once by the hive, I lowered the branch and swarm on to the white sheet. Taking a good hold of the end of the branch I lifted it and gave it two violent shakes to dislodge the cluster on to the sheet. Bees exploded into the air, but the majority fell on to the white sheet. I placed the branch on to the sheet and retired to see what would happen.

The bees were spread all over the sheet and though I did not see the queen, the bees started to walk up the ramp and into the hive. I knew that the queen would look for the dark entrance and once in, the others would follow. It was great to see this army of bees some walking, some running up the white sheet and into the hive. Over a period of about a half an hour most of the bees had disappeared in. Many were also clustered on the outside wall of the hive and some were still on the branch. A couple more shakes dislodged them and like the others they walked up the ramp. I gave a bit of smoke to some stragglers and then I informed the wedding party that we should leave them and I would return at dusk.

I returned as it was getting dark to find that no bees were left on the sheet and a few were flying around the hive. I gave the air around the hive a few puffs of smoke and though a handful of bees would not go in, I sealed the entrance with gaffer tape, pleased with myself having collected the vast majority. I needed now to make the hive safe to transport home in my car. Using two ratchet straps I strapped the hive so it could not come apart, then lifted it on to a large dust sheet which was large enough to gather up and tie together at the top. Once this was completed I loaded the hive into the car.

Once home I unwrapped the sheet, removed the straps and placed the hive in my chosen location and unsealed the entrance. By now it was dark and I decided to place the feeder the following morning, as the bees would not leave even if they wanted to before then. Next morning I fitted a rapid feeder, feeding them a 1:1 sugar solution and I left this on for a number of days, feeding them until they had drawn out much of the wax foundation. I am pleased to say this colony did not vacate their new home and are thriving well.

In this instance I had an empty hive. However the chances are you may not have one available. Naturally it depends on where you locate the swarm, but getting it into a box will enable you to get it home and give you time to sort out the hiving. If the swarm is in a position where you can get a skep or even a large cardboard box over the bees, smoking below them will encourage them to climb up into it. Having taken in a few days' supply of feed, bees when they swarm are actually quiet docile. Since collecting this

swarm, I have now collected two further swarms. One, using a box over the cluster and smoking them into a nucleus box hanging from a tree, the second brushing them into a container. For this swarm I placed a wine box with a small white cloth covered ramp leading to the holes I had drilled into it. As I swept the bees into a container I emptied this over the ramp and the bees happily climbed up and into it.

Once contained, with the box sealed and wrapped in a securely tied sheet, it is easy to transport them home in your car. Once home, if you need time to prepare a hive, place the sheeted box on the ground, untie it and make a small entrance by placing a block under one corner of the box. The bees will soon settle and treat this as their new home. The only problem is you cannot feed them. However, doing this will give you some extra time to prepare a new hive for them. Once you are ready to hive them, the preferred method is to shake them out to allow them to climb into the hive via a sheeted ramp. However, another quick method is to open the hive, remove the crown board and dump the colony from the box straight over the frames. Not very dignified, but as long as the queen goes into the hive the rest of the bees will follow.

WARNING!

I have found that swarms are attracted to apiaries. So you may find during the swarming season that a number of swarms may cluster close by to your hive location. Good to collect, if you want to create new hives or to pass on to new beekeepers that are looking for bees.

A perfectly shaped swarm cluster low down on a garden bush.

Your second year

"the spring clean"

With spring arriving and your bees busy bringing in nectar and pollen, you will need to give your hives a spring clean. Bees like clean living and will keep their hives relatively clean.

However some assistance from us will help in keeping the hive disease free. As it is the start of your second season, the spring clean is not too complicated, but some forward thinking and planning will make certain you have everything with you when you open the hive.

Wait for a warm sunny day and although warmer than it will have been, you will want to work quickly so as not to let the heat escape from the hive. This is not an inspection, though naturally you will keep an eye open as you work through the hive. Other than your normal equipment of bee suit, smoker and hive tool, you will need the following items:

1. New or cleaned wire mesh floor and entrance block
2. New or cleaned brood box
3. New or cleaned dummy board
4. New or cleaned crown board

Once ready to open the hive, have everything at hand alongside the clean brood box with it sitting on blocks off the ground. I also place a mite board under the blocks to catch any bees which might fall. Remove the roof and crown board from the hive to be cleaned, leaning the crown board against the entrance. Remove the dummy board and place it in the roof. Then remove each frame, placing them in exactly the same position in the clean brood box. As you lift out each frame, you should notice the first few and the last few frames have capped food stores. This and the position of any other food stores will give you a good indication on whether your bees need any spring feeding. As you get closer to the central frames you should see capped brood cells with capped honey above the brood. If this is the case, then the food is ideally positioned close to where the queen is laying her eggs. If there is honey on the outer frames but a limited amount of capped food close to any brood, I would suggest giving the hive a spring feed.

This process of exchanging the frames from the used brood box to a new or cleaned one should only take you a minute or two. Once the frame transfer is completed, remove the old empty brood box and the used wire mesh floor. Put in place the clean mesh floor and entrance block and then place the clean brood box containing the transferred frames on top. Lever the frames gently into their position and place a clean dummy board as the last frame. Before closing the hive give the old brood box, dummy board and crown board a firm shake over the frames to dislodge any bees still clinging to them. To close the hive add a clean crown board, cover the feed holes and finally fit the roof. Your bees now have a nice clean home. There will still be bees clinging on to the old hive parts, leave these leaning against the entrance and as the day cools these bees will soon make their way home to join the rest. You can then return at dusk to collect these hive parts.

Lightly toast corners and cracks with a blow torch to kill any bugs and diseases.

In subsequent years you will annually do this spring clean. However you may also need to replace old frames of brood comb which has discoloured, but at this stage it is not something to worry about. Depending on the weather conditions each spring, you may find that things are progressing rapidly at this stage in the hive. Indications are seeing plenty of capped brood and even a build up of burr comb on the underside of the crown board. If this is the case, your bees might need a bit more room for expansion. As written earlier, it is better to place a super too early than too late. If you feel that your bees could do with the space, add a queen excluder on to the brood box with a sheet of newspaper over it and place a super with frames on top. If you have some frames from last year of which the wax foundation has been drawn out, help your bees and place 3 or 4 frames in the super. Alternate these frames between new foundation and the drawn frames. The newspaper is there

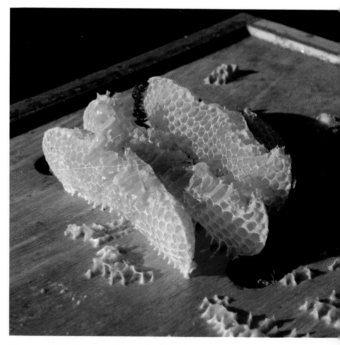

Burr comb built up on the underside of the crown board.

to act as insulation, as the super above will be cold. This is just like insulation in your attic at home, with the rooms below warm, but your attic quiet cold. As the days warm and your bees want to expand upwards they will soon chew holes through the paper to allow them access into the super. When you do your first full inspection of the year and see that the bees are using the super, you can remove what remains of the newspaper.

Having removed the used brood box, floor and crown board, you can clean them to reuse or to start another hive. You will see that your bees have deposited propolis in all the corners and edges. It is sticky and messy, but use your hive tool to remove this and any burr comb. Using a blow torch, lightly toast the inside corners and gaps thus killing any potential bugs and diseases which might be harbouring there. You only need to burn to a light coffee colour to these areas with your blow torch, not set the wood on fire. With the torching done, I give the outside of the wood a quick rub over with some fine sandpaper. This removes any dirt and mould which has collected on the hive whilst it has been subjected to the elements. You can then treat the timber with a wood preservative making the hive parts look new again.

Hives are not cheap, so a little extra work now will see your hives last many years. That said it is worth remembering that red cedar will last for years without being treated with preservatives.

Hints & tips

- In early spring the position of the bee's food is very important – feed if necessary.

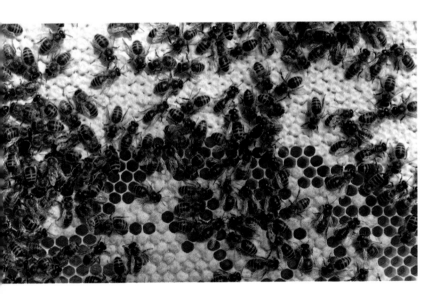

Above: Capped honey close to new brood.

Swarm prevention in your second season

"splitting a hive"

As spring turns to summer and your bees are rapidly collecting nectar and pollen, you will see during your weekly inspections that the brood box is filling with frames full of larvae and capped brood. Though you have added a super or two to give your bees more space, the brood box, as bees hatch, will become very congested and the bee's natural instinct is to divide the colony.

Creating an artificial swarm

Swarming can occur with half of the colony vacating the hive to look for a new home. As beekeepers, losing half the colony will not help us to maximize our honey harvest, so we need to take steps to prevent the hive swarming.

As the colony increases in size, the bees will produce queen cells to produce a new queen. Then just before a new queen hatches, the old queen will depart taking half the colony with her. The new virgin queen having hatched will soon mate and the remaining bees will continue foraging and feeding the new eggs that she has laid. But of course now the numbers in the colony are half what they were.

Bees generally swarm through May, June and July, so near the end of April and through this period you need to keep a very close eye for queen cells when doing your inspections. When you see queen cells forming, you can pinch or cut them out; however doing this will not prevent the bees continuing to produce queen cells. The more you remove them, the harder they will become to spot, as bees are very adept at hiding them away so we cannot find them.

If you allow the bees to build queen cells and do not remove them they are reasonably easy to spot. Being about an inch in size and resembling a large acorn, they are usually found hanging in the

A queen cell hanging from the middle of a frame.

middle of a frame of brood or on the bottom edge of a frame. They can be a single cell or in a row of 2 or 3. If you do spot them, then you will need to act to prevent your hive from swarming. From the laying of the egg to the virgin queen hatching is 16 days, however the colony will swarm soon after the cell is capped, which is approximately 8 days from when the egg was laid. So inspecting your hives weekly should enable you to spot and prevent swarming within this time period.

As beekeepers we need to split the hive, tricking the bees into thinking they have swarmed themselves. To do this is not difficult, however a bit of pre-planning helps when creating an artificial swarm, so make certain you have everything you require to split the hive.

Equipment you will need:
1. Clean wire mesh floor and stand
2. Clean entrance block
3. Clean brood box with frames of foundation
4. 2 Clean queen excluders

First place the above list of equipment alongside the hive you are going to split. Place the clean wire mesh floor and stand alongside the hive you are working on and in the position where you wish the new hive to be. Open the hive, as you would do for any other inspection and go through each frame in the brood box. You need to find the queen plus the location of any queen cells. Remove one new frame of foundation from the centre of the new clean brood box and lay this to one side. Having located the queen, carefully remove the frame she is on with the capped brood and bees, placing it in the space you have made in the new brood box.

Remove the old brood box with the queen cells and place this to one side, on blocks, as this is to go on to the new clean wire mesh floor and stand

Place a queen excluder on the old wire mesh floor and put the new clean brood box with the queen and frames with new foundation on top of this, then add another queen excluder above the brood box. You will now have the queen in her original hive position. The excluders are in place top and bottom, to prevent her from eloping should she wish to. You can now add any supers you had in place back on top before adding the crown board and roof. Your original queen is now safely in the hive still in her original location.

Next place the old brood box on top of the new mesh floor in the new hive position and slowly go through each frame, shaking off the bees except from the frame with the queen cell you wish to keep. When choosing the queen cell you want to hatch, choose one in which you can see a larva inside rather than one which is nearly capped. This way you know that there is something inside. Remember which frame has your chosen queen cell, before checking that there are not more queen cells which you might have missed. Shaking off the bees will help you to see the frames and brood more clearly. It is vital not to shake the queen cell you wish to keep as this could damage or dislodge the larva. Should you find any or are suspicious that you might be seeing the construction of any other ones, pinch or cut these out. Once you are happy that only the one queen cell exists, replace a frame of new foundation in the gap you removed the queen from then you can close up this hive. You have now successfully split the hive.

Hints & tips
- Place brood boxes or supers on blocks, so they do not come in contact with the ground.

A marked queen bee laying an egg in a cell.

To recap, you now have two hives. One hive with the queen in her original position and a new second hive, with a queen cell which will hatch in a few days. As the day progresses the bees which were foraging, will return to find their queen. Any other foraging bees which are now in the second hive will depart returning to the position of their original hive. The new hive will be left with young nurse bees and most of the brood from the original hive. These young nurse bees have never flown and having never left the hive do not know that their location has been changed.

The original hive will now think they have swarmed naturally as the size of the colony is now dramatically reduced. The queen on only one frame of brood will want to continue laying eggs, so the bees within the hive will rapidly be drawing out the wax foundation in the other frames to produce comb for her to lay in. Though there will be no food in the brood box, the supers on top will have enough food in them to see the bees through this period until the foundation is drawn out, the queen is laying and they have placed food stocks close by. Leave the hive for a couple of weeks and then continue doing your weekly inspections.

Within the new hive, the nurse bees will continue feeding any uncapped larvae and as they mature will soon be out foraging themselves. The capped brood will continue hatching to become the new nurse bees. Within a few days the queen cell will hatch and from hatching, your virgin queen will have flown and mated, returning to the hive to start her cycle of egg laying. Leave the hive for a couple weeks after the queen has hatched and then do a quick inspection to see if she has started laying eggs, though it may take 3 weeks before you see any. Though the colony will increase with hatching brood and space might become tight again, it is unlikely they will swarm. After this 2 to 3 week period and you are seeing new brood, then you can add supers to aid them with space.

Ideally your new hive will be placed in the location you require it. In one of my cases, I wanted the new hive to be about 100 metres away in another location. If this is the case, leave the hive alone for a couple of days, allowing any of the foraging bees to find their way back to the queen in the original hive. After a couple of days, late one evening, I sealed the entrance of the new hive, strapped the hive and stand together with ratchet straps. With a friend, slowly and carefully we moved it the 100 metres to its new location, being careful not to damage the queen cell. Once in place I opened the entrance and now the hive was in place to continue its production.

Remember though, should you be unable to move the hive within this 2 day period, that the bees as they mature will soon be out foraging and the new queen may not have hatched and mated yet. If this is case, you will need to leave the hive in place for 3 weeks to allow her time to mate. You don't want to be in the situation of the queen being out of the hive mating and returning to find the hive is not there. Be patient and should you still wish to relocate the hive, you will first have to move it to a site over three miles away for 2 weeks, before bringing it back to your new location.

One note of caution, as I experienced, was a cold weekend having made the hive split. The young nurse bees will have food within the hive, but much of this will be capped and to make it easier for them to get to a supply of food, I fitted a rapid feeder with 1:1 sugar solution for a couple of days. Possibly this was not necessary, however as before with feeding, the bees will only take it if they need it.

Creating a nucleus

You may decide that you do not wish to have further hives, but still need to take steps to prevent your hive swarming. Another method is to create a nucleus which you can give or sell on to another beekeeper. Your local association will have a growing list of new beekeepers desperate to get hold of their first colony of bees.

Creating a 5 frame nucleus is simple, but you will need to have a nucleus box to make the transfer. Whoever takes delivery of the nucleus should return the box to you with new frames of foundation, having transferred the bees on frames into their hive.

To create the nucleus, place the empty nucleus box on blocks alongside the hive you are going to split. Open the hive and go through each frame slowly to search for the queen and any queen cells. You only want one queen cell to remain in the hive, so pinch or cut out any others. The frame with the queen cell needs to remain in the hive, so remember where this is. You need to give the nucleus some food stores, so select a couple of frames of brood which have some capped stores and place in the nucleus as the first and fifth frame. Transfer the frame of brood with the queen on to the centre of the nucleus and then add to two further frames of brood and bees. With the transfer made, place the lid on to the nucleus box.

Above: A nucleus of bees with a feeder in place, ready for a collection by a new beekeeper.

Opposite inset: A queen cup within a frame.

In your original hive, you will need to replace the removed frames with new frames of wax foundation. Once these are in place, you can close the hive with the queen excluder and supers in place as they were before.

The nucleus box has mesh holes for ventilation, but make certain you open the entrance hole. The box can now remain in place until it is collected, ideally on the same day. It is best if the new beekeeper waits until evening to collect their nucleus, allowing any foraging bees to have returned for the day. At dusk once all the bees have returned, seal the entrance and screw or strap down the lid. The nucleus can now be safely transported in the back of a car. The new owner of the colony on getting them home, places the nucleus it their chosen location and can transfer them into their hive in 24 hours time.

Hints & tips

- Golden rule is you can move a hive up to 3 feet or over 3 miles – nothing in between.

97

Extracting honey

"the sticky but sumptuous bit"

After all your efforts looking after your bees, your reward is all the delicious honey you are going to harvest. No doubt having told friends and family about your hobby, they are all queuing up waiting for their first jar of honey.

Above: Honey dripping from an uncapped comb.

Opposite: Brushing bees from a frame of honey comb "Brush and Run".

Removing supers

To harvest the honey in the supers, you first have to check that the bees have reduced the water content. You will know this when inspecting your hives and can see the frames in the supers are capped with a white wax. As with all aspects of beekeeping think ahead and make a plan. Before removing the filled supers you need to have prepared all the equipment you will need and decided on a room to do the extraction. As a hobby beekeeper this will most likely be your kitchen. Extracting honey can be a messy business; however cleaning up afterwards is not hard with hot water and a sponge.

Before removing the supers from the hive you first need to remove the bees from within the supers. If your bees have been collecting pollen and nectar from a variety of sources then this can be done simply using an ingenious device, called a Porter Bee Escape. However, if your bees have been primarily on oil seed rape, you will have to use the method known as the "brush and run".

Having decided which day you wish to do your honey extraction, you will need to fit Porter Bee Escapes to your hives, 24 hours in advance. To do this, remove the queen excluder placing a crown board between the brood box and supers, with the bee escapes in place. If you do not have a spare crown board use the one in place on the hive and for this short period you can cover the top super with a cloth before fitting the roof.

Above: Porter Bee Escape in place on a crown board.

Opposite: Uncapping a frame of honey using a capping fork.

Previous page: A full frame of capped honey.

Hints & tips

- A super full of honey is heavy (25lbs – 11kg) so have a wheel or sack barrow with you if you have to carry any distance.

Porter Bee Escapes are one way valves. On top of your crown board are two holes which you will have kept covered unless feeding your bees, it is into these holes that you put the Porter Bee Escapes. Once in place any bees which are working within the super will descend into the hive to collect further stores or to go out foraging. As they go through the bee escape a spring clip enables them to exit, but stops them returning. After 24 hours when you return to remove the supers, you should find the supers empty of bees. Any lingering bees, should there be any, can be easily brushed off. Cover the supers with a cloth and you should be able to get them inside without too many bees following you.

If your bees have been or could have been on oil seed rape, then Porter Bee Escapes cannot be used. Once bees have left the super, the honey will cool, unfortunately with oil seed rape honey, this cooling sets the honey which makes it impossible to extract. Therefore extracting oil seed rape honey has to be done immediately the supers have been removed from the hive. You do not want bees on the frames when extracting, so the "brush and run" method has to be used. When you come to remove the honey, it will help if you have an empty super. It will also help you greatly if there are two of you to carry out this procedure. With the empty super placed on a cloth, remove, shake and brush each frame of honey to dislodge the bees back into the hive. Pass the frame to your partner, who places it in the empty super and immediately covers with another cloth. Carry out this procedure for each frame, until you have removed all the frames. Any bees close by will be attracted by the honey, so keep the supers covered and take indoors for immediate extraction.

Extracting the honey

With your full supers indoors, the first job before spinning the frames in an extractor is to remove the wax capping. Bee equipment suppliers offer all manner of tools to carry this out, but the two most used methods are either using a sharp flexible knife or an uncapping fork. Both methods work well and are helped if you have a bowl of hot water to dip them into between each cut or scrape.

Place the frame of honey on to a flat tray, I use a paint roller tray, as this holds the frame allowing you to remove the wax cappings on both sides and catches any honey which drips from the cells as you are doing this. You only have to take off the wax capping, so gently but firmly remove these without going too deep and removing comb and honey also. Have an empty bowl alongside you, which you can scrape all the wax cappings

Above: Four frames of honey in a tangential extractor.

Opposite: Uncapped frame of honey comb.

into. These cappings can be filtered to collect the residue of honey on them and the remaining wax can later be melted down to make candles, wax polish or even sold in exchange for new sheets of foundation. You may find sides of a frame which you can see honey in, but have not been capped. A test to see that this honey has had its water content reduced allowing you to extract it, is to give it a firm shake. If no honey drips out then you can extract it, if honey does drip out then return it to the bees to complete and cap.

Whether you have bought, borrowed or hired an extractor make certain it is very clean and dry before placing the frames inside it to spin. The smaller tabletop extractors usually are tangential, which means that each frame when spun has to be removed and turned before extracting the other side. Place the frames in the extractor as per the extractor's instructions. A frame of honey is heavy, so with the lid in place, start spinning slowly and as the honey spins out you can increase the speed as each turn will become lighter. After spinning for a minute remove and turn round the frames to extract the other side. Do not try and spin out completely all the honey on one side. If you try to empty one side whilst the other is still full it can crush through the frame. It takes more work but extracting a little from each side keeps the frames when spinning, balanced.

The empty frames of comb can then be returned to the super you removed them from. Continue through each of the frames you have to extract, keeping an eye on the level of honey in the bottom of the extractor. Once the level is high enough, the extractors honey gate can be opened to pour the honey through filters into a honey bucket.

You have a choice of how many and how fine a filter you wish to pour your honey through. Most beekeepers pass the honey through a coarse and fine filter which should remove any debris in the

honey. The more times you pour the honey the more air will get into it. It is therefore essential having completed the extraction, that all the honey in buckets or a honey tank sits for a minimum of 24 hours to allow the air bubbles to rise to the surface.

Having completed the extraction the empty frames of comb can be returned to the hives and the bees will clean them. Wait until the evening when you return them, so that the bees don't get over excited. If you have extracted honey early in the season the bees will clean the comb and continue to fill them with honey for you to harvest later in the season. However, if this was the last extraction of the season, allow the bees to clean the comb for two or three days, by placing the supers on the hive with the crown board below them. Open one of the crown board holes a fraction to allow the bees access. Due to

the small opening the bees will think that this is not their own honey stores and will clean the comb taking any residue honey down into the brood box. After a couple of days put in place Porter Bee Escapes to clear the bees from the supers or lift off the cleaned supers and stack them outside, not too close to the hive and any lingering bees will return to the hive during the evening. Once the cleaned supers and frames are clear of bees they can be cleaned to store away for winter.

Hints & tips

- After extracting, your honey must sit for a minimum of 24 hours before pouring into jars

Honey

"jars, chunk or comb"

Having let your honey settle you can now pour it into jars. Jars of all shapes and sizes can be purchased or you can use clean jars you have collected. Most honey is sold in 1lb or 454 gm jars and if selling needs to be clearly marked with some details showing weight, who and where the honey came from, plus the country of origin. Each country has its own food labelling rules. These rules should be available on the internet through your local government office dealing with food quality and hygiene.

Pour the honey through the honey gate on your honey tank, into the jars and screw the cap on immediately. With practise you will find that this can be done quickly judging the level to be at the correct weight per jar or weigh them using kitchen digital scales. Once all the honey is in jars you can apply the labels before storing them at room temperature in a dark place.

You may like to do some jars of chunk honey; if so, keep a couple of frames back from extraction. Cut out chunks of honey comb and place these in the jars before topping the jar up with the liquid honey. If you like comb honey on its own, you can purchase un-wired foundation, which cannot be used in an extractor. Plastic or wooden containers for comb honey can be bought and are an attractive way to sell or to give away your honey as a present.

Left: Pouring honey into jars from a honey tank.
Opposite: Liquid, comb and chunk honey.

If you are looking to sell your honey there are a few regulations, however generally if selling small quantities these are not prohibitive, but it would pay to check your local regulations, as basic food hygiene handling standards need to be observed.

Locally produced honey is in high demand, so you should be able to find a ready market for it. If you have passing traffic, a sign saying "Honey for Sale" will attract people to stop.

Local markets and farmers markets are another excellent way to sell your honey and the cost to have a table at one of these is not expensive. Your local shops may well be interested in selling some of your jars, however they will want a cut of the sale price. As a hobby beekeeper the quantity you have will not fill a supermarket, so you will probably sell some and give friends and family the rest. Remember though to keep a few of your own jars to enjoy yourself.

West Norfolk Fenland

Honey

454g 1lb   Produce of England

...d if its quality.
...so that the
...comes liquid.
...lowest power.
...the heating

A beekeeper's year

"things to remember to do"

Month by month notes

January
- Heft hives regularly to check weight
- Feed fondant as necessary
- Possibly treat Varroa with Oxalic Acid
- Check bees have access to water

February
- Heft hives regularly to check weight
- Feed fondant as necessary
- Possibly treat Varroa with Oxalic Acid
- Ensure bees have access to water
- Feed sugar syrup to weak colonies
- Add Fumidol B if Nosema suspected
- Construct new hives and prepare equipment

March
- Feed sugar syrup to weak colonies
- Add Fumidol B if Nosema suspected
- Ensure bees have access to water
- Construct new hives and prepare equipment

Bees love oil seed rape but remove the honey quickly.

April
- Feed sugar syrup to weak colonies
- Spring clean - Change floors, brood box and crown board
- Any suspected diseases get second opinion
- Add first supers to hive
- Monitor for Varroa

May
- Feed sugar syrup if foraging conditions are poor
- Check hives every 7-9 days for queen cells
- Split hives and make up artificial swarms

June

- Feed sugar syrup if foraging conditions are poor
- Mark queens
- Check hives every 7-9 days for queen Cells
- Split hives and make up artificial swarms
- Add supers well in advance to prevent congestion
- Extract Oil Seed Rape honey

July

- Feed sugar syrup if foraging conditions are poor
- Check hives every 7-9 days for queen cells
- Check for space, disease, stores, queen and swarming
- Add supers
- Extract Blossom honey

August

- Feed sugar syrup if foraging conditions are poor
- Check hives every 7-9 days for space, disease etc.
- Add supers
- Extract Blossom honey
- Cull and replace old queens
- Prevent robbing bees and wasps
- Treat for Varroa once supers are removed
- Feed sugar syrup after Varroa treatment

September

- Treat for Varroa once supers are removed
- Feed sugar syrup after Varroa treatment
- Prevent robbing bees and wasps
- Cull and replace old queens

October

- Complete winter feeding
- Prepare hives for winter - ventilation, mouse guards, woodpecker prevention etc.
- Clean and repair equipment

November

- Complete winter feeding
- Heft hives regularly to check weight
- Ensure bees have access to water

December

- Heft hives regularly to check weight
- Check hives for wind, rain damage etc
- Ensure bees have access to water
- Order new equipment for following year

The end

"if you have got to this stage, congratulations you are a beekeeper"

Conclusion

I hope you, the reader, have enjoyed this book and have found each stage in beekeeping easy to follow. There are so many more aspects to beekeeping which perhaps I could have added. However, I felt this would over complicate matters and many of these aspects come with years of beekeeping experience. I believe in trying to keep it simple and that even with a few decades of beekeeping under our belts, you and I will still be learning. I at times have been completely baffled by what my bees are doing. Rather than tear my hair out, I have come to the conclusion that when you feel this, that it is best to leave them alone. Bees are wild creatures and have been on this planet far longer than us, evolving quite successfully without our meddling.

As I complete this book, it is now June and I have six colonies in hives which are strong, filling the supers with honey and I have made my first extraction of the year. I also have two colonies in nucleuses, from swarms I have caught, which are waiting for new beekeepers to collect. Following a call, I have been to see another swarm clustered in a tree. Though this time, I am leaving it, as it is too high and not affecting anyone plus I have no more hives or nucleus boxes to fit them into. I will just take some photographs and in their own time they will find their own home.

Glossary

A

Abscond
The action of bees that leave the hive suddenly, leaving the hive empty.

Alighting board
Slope in front of entrance for bees to land on before entering hive. Also known as a landing board.

American foul brood (AFB)
A viral disease affecting bee brood, it is highly contagious and has a long life span.

Anaphylactic shock
A strong and possibly fatal reaction to bee stings.

Apiarist
A beekeeper.

Apiary
The area or location where bees and hives are kept.

Apiculture
The science and study and possibly art of keeping bees.

Apiguard
A miticide used to control Varroa mites.

Apiphobia
The acute fear of bees or anything related to bees.

Apis mellifera
The scientific name of the Italian honey bee or European honey bee.

Apistan
A miticide used to control Varroa mites.

Apitherapy
A division of therapy that uses bees and bee products for therapeutic and medical purposes.

Artificial swarm
Splitting a hive to trick the bees into thinking they have swarmed themselves.

B

Bee bread
Pollen that was collected by bees and then mixed with various solutions including honey which is stored within a cell of the comb. This is a high protein feed for both the developing larvae and bees.

Bee brush
A long handled soft haired brush to gently move bees.

Bee glue
Propolis - A sticky resinous material that bees collect from plants and use to strengthen hive comb and fill cracks within the hive.

Beehive
A container used by a beekeeper for the purpose of keeping a colony of bees.

Beeswax
A substance that is secreted by glands on the worker bee. This is the primary building material used by bees to build comb.

Brace comb
The sections of seemingly random comb that connect hive parts together. Brace Comb is a form of Burr comb.

Brood
A general term to refer to immature bees, includes egg, larvae and pupae.

Brood box, deep box or chamber
Section of the hive where brood is being raised and where the queen lays her eggs.

Brood food
A highly nutritious glandular secretion from the worker bee that is used to feed both brood and the queen.

Burr comb
Any section of comb that is not a part of the main comb piece within the frame or hanging from the top bar.

C

Capped brood
Cells on the comb containing bee larvae that is fully enclosed by a wax capping.

Capping
A thin layer of wax that covers cells containing honey or brood.

Cast swarm
A second swarm from a hive after colony has swarmed once already.

Caste
A name for the existence of different classifications of bees of a specific family. Include queen, drone and worker.

Cell
A single hexagonal prismatic chamber that makes up comb. Cells are used to store honey, pollen, nectar and developing brood.

Chalk brood
A fungal infection of the brood, the cells look like they are filled with chalk.

Chunk honey
A jar of honey with a chunk of comb honey in it.

Cleansing flight
The flight made by a bee to cleanse its digestive track after a long period of confinement. Usually during winter.

Cluster
A mass of bees, often referring to a swarm or when huddled together for winter.

Colony
A collection or family of bees living within a single social unit.

Colony collapse disorder
A major plague affecting whole colonies of bees. At present mainly in the USA.

Comb
A double sided configuration of hexagonal cells made of beeswax. Used by the bees to store food and raise brood.

Comb honey
A chunk of honey cut from the comb.

Commercial
A type of hive or a professional beekeeper.

Contact feeder
A bucket with mesh opening used to feed bees.

Crown board
Ceiling of the hive with holes to allow feeding.

D

Dadant
A type of hive.

Deep box
Section of the hive where brood is being raised and where the queen lays her eggs.

Drawn comb
Comb which contains completed cells drawn out of the wax foundation.

Drone
A male bee.

Dummy board
A solid wood frame to prevent rolling of bees when inspecting hive.

E

Eke
A shallow frame of wood the same size as a hive, used to enable spacing for treatments or feeding.

Entrance block
Wooden entrance to a hive which can be adjusted.

European foul brood
A viral disease which affects the bee brood.

Extraction
Removal of honey from the comb.

Extractor
A centrifugal machine in which honey is spun from the frames.

Feeders
Appliances used to feed bees artificially.

Fondant
Icing sugar used as a feed supplement.

Foragers
The bees which leave the hive to collect pollen and nectar.

Foul brood
Generic term to describe a bacterial disease that affects brood.

Foundation
A thin sheet of wax that is embossed to be used as a guide for comb creation by the bees. Can be wired or unwired.

Frame
A rectangular segment made of four slats of wood that is made to contain comb.

Fumadil B
An antibiotic used to control Nosema which is sold under the trade name of Fumadil B.

Fumagillin
An antibiotic used to control Nosema which is sold under the trade name of Fumadil B.

Guard bee
A bee which remains at the entrance of a hive protecting it from invaders.

Guarding
The action of a bee which detects invaders and examines entering bees.

Heft/hefting
Lifting a corner of a hive to feel weight and how much food is in the hive.

Hive
Home for an individual colony of managed bees.

Hive tool
A bladed and hooked bar used by the beekeeper to maintain and manage a hive.

Hoffman self spacing frame
Frames that have the end bars wider at the top than the bottom providing the correct spacing when frames are placed in a hive.

Honey bucket
Container used to collect and settle honey after extraction.

Honey comb
Comb that has been nearly or completely filled with honey.

Honey flow
A period of time when an abundance of nectar is available to be collected and converted into honey.

Landing board
Slope in front of entrance for bees to land on before entering hive. Also known as an alighting board.

Langstroft
A type of hive.

Larva/larvae
The second stage of development in the life cycle of the bee.

Laying worker
An unfertilized, non queen female bee that is capable of laying drone eggs. This is often the result of a hive remaining queenless for a period of time.

Mandibles
Are the bees pliers, for cutting, gripping and to hold enemies in a fight.

Marked queen
A queen bee that has been marked with a spot of paint.

Mesh floor
Wire mesh floor below brood box to allow debris and dead mites to fall through.

Miticide
A chemical or biological agent which is applied to a colony to control parasitic mites.

Mouse guard
Metal entrance attached to hive entrance to prevent entry by mice.

N

National
A type of hive.

Nectar
A food source high in carbohydrates, which occurs naturally in the nectarines of a flower.

Nectar flow
The mass gathering of nectar from flowers by bees.

Nest
An unmanaged wild colony of bees. Often found in the hollow of a tree, wall partition, attic, etc.

Nosema
An illness that affects the digestive track in bees.

Nuc or nucleus box/hive
A small colony of bees housed within a smaller hive container with 5 or 6 frames.

Nuptial flight
The mating flight taken by a queen to mate with a variety of drones.

Nurse bee
Young hive bound bee that feeds and cares for the larvae.

P

Pheromone
A chemical scent produced to establish a basic form of communication or to stimulate response.

Pollen
The powdery substance produced by the male segment of a flower.

Porter bee escape
A device fitted to a crown board just before extraction of honey. A one way valve enables the clearing of bees from a super.

Propolis
A sticky resinous material that bees collect from plants and use to strengthen hive comb and fill cracks within the hive.

Pupae
The final stage in a brood bee's metamorphosis.

Q

Queen
The fertile female bee that once mated should be capable of producing male and female offspring.

Queen cage
A device used to trap the queen to enable her to be marked.

Queen clipping
Removing a portion of one or both front wings of a queen to prevent her from flying.

Queen cup
A cup-shaped cell hanging vertically from the comb, but containing no egg.

Queen excluder
A device used to prevent the larger queen bee and drones from passing through.

R

Rapid feeder
A container placed on a hive to feed bees.

Robbing bee
Foreign bee attempting to steal honey from a hive.

Royal jelly
A substance produced by worker bees to feed to youngest brood and to the queen brood throughout its immature life.

S

Scout bee
A bee which is responsible for finding a new home for a swarm of bees.

Sealed
Honey or brood which has been capped with a thin layer of wax.

Skep
A wicker basket used to collect swarms.

Smith
A type of hive.

Smoker
A tool to blow cool smoke over your hive.

Solar wax extractor
Glass-covered insulated box used to melt wax from combs and cappings using the heat of the sun.

Splitting a hive
Method used to create an artificial swarm, tricking the bees into thinking they have swarmed themselves.

Sting
The defence mechanism of a bee that is capable of releasing venom into its victim.

Sugar solution
A mixture of dissolved sugar and water fed to bees.

Super
A box placed on a hive with frames to collect honey.

Supering
The act and process of adding supers to a hive in an effort to collect honey to harvest.

Supersede/supersedure
The natural process of a colony of bees replacing its queen with a new one.

Swarm
A collection of bees that is currently without a home site and looking for a new one.

T

Terramycin
An antibiotic used for the treatment of bacterial disease.

Top bar
The top part of a frame.

Top bar hive
A type of hive originally found in Africa.

U

Uncapping knife or fork
Tools used to shave off the wax cappings of sealed honey prior to extraction.

Uncapping tank
Container over which frames of honey are uncapped and used to collect any residue honey.

V

Varroa
A parasitic mite which attaches itself to bees.

Veil
A protective netting that covers the beekeepers face.

Virgin queen
An unmated queen bee.

W

Waggle dance
A figure of 8 motion carried out by bees to indicate location of a pollen/nectar source.

Wax moth
Galleria mellonella – a moth whose larvae bore through and destroy honeycomb.

WBC
A type of hive.

Winter cluster
A tightly packed cluster of bees that forms to maintain warmth during the colder winter months.

Worker
An unfertilised female bee that constitutes as the majority of a colony's population.

Website links

United Kingdom

www.britishbee.org.uk

Department for Environment Food and Rural Affairs
www.defra.gov.uk/foodfarm/growing/bees/index.htm

Food and Environment Research Agency
www.fera.defra.gov.uk

Scotland

www.scottishbeekeepers.org.uk

Wales

www.wbka.com

Northern Ireland

www.ubka.org

Ireland

www.irishbeekeeping.ie

Australia

www.honeybee.com.au

Canada

www.honeycouncil.ca

New Zealand

www.nba.org.nz

United States

www.abfnet.org

USDA Agricultural Research Department
www.ars.usda.gov

South Africa

www.beekeepers.co.za

France

www.unaf.net

Germany

www.deutscherimkerbund.de

Italy

www.cra-api.it

United Kindom

E.H. Thorne
www.thorne.co.uk

Paynes Bee Farm
www.paynesbeefarm.co.uk

Maisemore Apiaries
www.bees-online.co.uk

National Bee Supplies
www.beekeeping.co.uk

Fragile Planet
www.fragile-planet.co.uk

Beechwood Bees
www.beechwoodbees.co.uk

Easy Bee Products
www.easybeeproducts.co.uk

Park Bee Keeping Supplies
www.parkbeekeeping.com

Ireland

Shanvaus Apiaries
www.shanvaus-apiary-online.net

Australia

Penders Beekeeping Supplies
www.penders.net.au

Redpaths Beekeeping Supplies
www.redpaths.com.au

Bob's Beekeeping Supplies
www.bobsbeekeeping.com.au

Bindaree Bee Supplies
www.bindaree.com.au

Canada

The Bee Works
www.beeworks.com

Countryfields Bee Keeping Supplies
www.countryfields.ca

Benson Beekeeping Supplies
www.bensonbee.com

Better Bee Supplies
www.betterbees.com

Munro Honey
www.munrohoney.com

Vancouver Island Apiary Supplies
www.thebeestore.com

New Zealand

Ecroyd Beekeeping Supplies
www.ecroyd.com

Ceracell Beekeeping Supplies
www.bees.co.nz

United States

Betterbee
www.betterbee.com

Mann Lake
www.mannlakeltd.com

Beecare
www.beecare.com

Brushy Mountain Bee Farm
www.brushymountainbeefarm.com

Arnold Honey Bee Services
www.arnoldhoneybeeservices.com

South Africa

Honeybadger
www.honeybadger.co.za

Beeware Beekeeping Supplies
www.beeware.co.za

France

Ickowicz Apiculture
www.ickowicz-apiculture.com

Luberon Apiculture
www.apiculture.net

Lapi
www.lapi.fr

Author and photographer: David Wootton

David is a Commercial Photographer based on his family's farm in the West Norfolk Fens. He purchased his first camera in 1977 and was a keen amateur. In 1989 whilst living in the French Alpine town of Chamonix, he discovered the relatively new sport of Paragliding. He soon discovered that whilst flying around the Mont Blanc region there was a market for his photographs of the sport taken from the air. Returning to the UK in 1994, he set up as a commercial photographer offering imagery to businesses to promote and market their company and products. David also specialises in aerial photography, annually doing site surveys for major companies in landfill, construction and quarrying. He has also covered much of the UK for the RSPB, photographing their bird reserves from the air.

David has travelled a great deal around the world on private projects and for magazine clients; covering diverse subjects such as - Orang Utans on Borneo, Tigers in India, The World's largest food fight: La Tomatina in Spain to name three. David's work has been published in over 200 magazines and newspapers worldwide plus numerous books. Married to Helen in 2008, he continues to live in Norfolk and took up beekeeping in 2009.

To view a broad range of David's photographic work, visit his website at:

www.dw-photography.co.uk
www.beekeeping-book.com

Photograph above by Paul Garner.

"There is no other field of animal husbandry like beekeeping. It has the appeal to the scientist, the nature lover and even (or especially) the philosopher. It is a chance to work with some of the most fascinating of God's creatures, to spend time and do work in the great outdoors, to challenge my abilities and continue to learn. My hope is that I never become so frail with old age that I cannot spend my days among the bees. It gives credence to the old saw that "the best things in life are free". I thank God daily for the opporunity and privilege to be a beekeeper".

Author Unknown

Colourful Dadant hives in the Jura mountain region of France.